# BRAIN WORKOUT:
# IQ Challenges

Terry Stickels & J.J. Mendoza Fernandez

## FALL RIVER PRESS

New York

# FALL RIVER PRESS

New York

An Imprint of Sterling Publishing
387 Park Avenue South
New York, NY 10016

The material in this book was previously published in
*Quick-to-Solve Brainteasers* by J.J. Mendoza Fernandez (pages 6-67)
and *Mind Workout Puzzles, Cunning Mind-Bending Puzzles, Devious Mind-Bending Puzzles,* and *Mesmerizing Mind-Bending Puzzles* by Terry Stickels (pages 67-167).

Book design by Ponderosa Pine Design
Cover design by Cattails Productions

ISBN 978-1-4351-4244-2

Distributed in Canada by Sterling Publishing
ᶜ/o Canadian Manda Group, 165 Dufferin Street
Toronto, Ontario, Canada M6K 3H6
Distributed in the United Kingdom by GMC Distribution Services
Castle Place, 166 High Street, Lewes, East Sussex, England BN7 1XU
Distributed in Australia by Capricorn Link (Australia) Pty. Ltd.
P.O. Box 704, Windsor, NSW 2756, Australia

For information about custom editions, special sales, and premium and corporate purchases, please contact Sterling Special Sales at 800-805-5489 or specialsales@sterlingpublishing.com.

Manufactured in the United States of America

2   4   6   8   10   9   7   5   3   1

www.sterlingpublishing.com

# CONTENTS

# INTRODUCTION

This book contains many different types of puzzle: numerical puzzles, logic puzzles, word games, lateral thinking puzzles, riddles, etc. The purpose of these puzzles is to entertain. The correct answer is not always obvious and this is one of the amusing aspects of this book. The reader will notice that the puzzles are often misleading or involve humor in the answer. Therefore, use your imagination, be alert, and have an open mind when trying to solve the puzzles.

## 1
How many times can you subtract 6 from 30?

## 2
What number can you subtract half from to obtain a result that is zero?

## 3
How can half of 12 be 7?

## 4
Find two whole, positive numbers that have a one-digit answer when multiplied and a two-digit answer when added.

## 5
Find two whole, positive numbers that have the same answer when multiplied together as when one is divided by the other.

## 6
Find two positive numbers that have the same answer when multiplied together as when added together.

## 7
Find a two-digit number that equals two times the result of multiplying its digits.

## 8

Find three whole, positive numbers that have the same answer when multiplied together as when added together.

## 9

What two two-digit numbers are each equal to their rightmost digit squared?

## 10

Find the highest number that can be written with three digits.

## COMPARING NUMBERS

## 11

The ages of a father and a son add up to 55. The father's age is the son's age reversed. How old are they?

## 12

How much do 10 pieces of candy cost if one thousand pieces cost $10?

## 13

An outlet and a light bulb cost $1.20. We know that the outlet costs $1 more than the light bulb. How much does each cost?

## 14

If 75% of all women are tall, 75% are brunette, and 75% are pretty, what is the minimum percentage of tall, brunette, pretty women?

## 15

Thirty-two students took a nationwide exam and all the students from New York passed it. If the students from New York made up exactly 5% of the total number of the students that passed the test, how many students passed it and how many students were from New York?

## 16

Of the 960 people in a theater, 17% tipped 5 cents to the usher, 50% of the remaining 83% tipped 10 cents, and the rest tipped nothing. How much did the usher get?

# OTHER NUMBERS

## 17

What must you do to make the equation below true?
81 × 9 = 801

## 18

There are 100 buildings along a street. A sign maker is ordered to number the buildings from 1 to 100. How many "9's" will he need?

## 19

How many tickets with different points of origination and destination can be sold on a bus line that travels a loop of 25 stops?

## 20

We know that humans have up to 100,000 hairs. In a city with more than 200,000 people, would it be possible to find two or more people with the same number of hairs?

# COUNTING

## 21

All my ties are red except two. All my ties are blue except two. All my ties are brown except two. How many ties do I have?

## 22

A street that's 30 yards long has a chestnut tree every 6 yards on both sides. How many chestnut trees are on the entire street?

## 23

A pet shop owner is in the countryside. If he says, "one bird per olive tree," there is one bird too many. However, if he says, "two birds per olive tree," there are no birds left over. How many birds and olive trees are there?

## 24

In a singles tennis tournament, 111 players participated. They used a new ball for each match. When a player lost one match, he was eliminated from the tournament. How many balls did they need?

## 25

Peter and John had a picnic. Peter had already eaten half of the muffins when John ate half of the remaining muffins plus three more. There were no muffins left. How many muffins did they take to the picnic?

## 26

A shepherd says to another, "If I give you one sheep, you will have twice the number of sheep that I have, but if you give me one, we will both have the same number of sheep." How many sheep did each shepherd have?

## 27

If I put in one canary per cage, I have one bird too many. However, if I put in two canaries per cage, I have one cage too many. How many cages and birds do I have?

## 28

If 1½ sardines cost 1½ dollars, how much would 7½ sardines cost?

## 29

If a brick weighs 3 pounds plus ½ a brick, what's the weight of 1½ bricks?

## 30

If 1½ dozen sardines costs 9½ dollars, how much do 18 sardines cost?

## 31

If 1½ men can eat 1½ pies in 1½ minutes, how many pies can 3 men eat in half an hour?

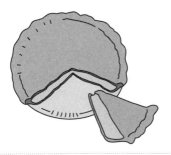

## 32

Yesterday afternoon, I went to visit my friend Albert, who is a painter. While I was watching him paint, I told him, "No wonder it takes you so long to finish a painting. Since I arrived, you have entered the studio twelve times." How many times did he leave the studio?

## 33

If two ducks are swimming in front of another duck, two ducks are swimming behind another duck, and one duck is swimming between two other ducks, what is the minimum number of ducks?

## 34

Two people are flipping coins. Each time, they bet $1 apiece. At the end, one person won $3 and the other one won three times. How many games did they play?

# MEASURING TIME, VOLUME, LENGTH, ETC.

## 35

A bottle with a cylindrical shape at the bottom and with an irregular shape at the top is filled halfway to the top with liquid. The cylindrical part contains approximately three-fourths of the capacity of the bottle and we wish to determine the exact percentage of liquid that the bottle contains. We cannot open it and we can only use a ruler. What must we do?

## 36

If one nickel is worth five cents, how much is half of one half of a nickel worth?

## 37

Two soldiers have been ordered to do the following chores:
1. Peel potatoes.
2. Do the dishes.
3. Mow the lawn.
Each of these chores, when done by one person, takes one hour. If they start at 8 a.m., what could they do to take as little time as possible if they have only one knife, one lawn mower, and one sink with room for one person?

## 38

A spider spins its web in a window frame. Each day, it spins an area equal to that of the amount already completed. It takes 30 days to cover the entire window frame. How long would two spiders take?

(In the case of two spiders, each of them spins an amount equal to the area of the existing part of the web made by that particular spider.)

## 39

We put a spore in a test tube. Every hour the spore divides into three parts, all the same size as the original part. If we put it in at 3 p.m., at 9 p.m. the tube will be completely full. At what time will the tube be one-third full?

## 40

How long is a rope that is 2 yards shorter than another rope that is three times the length of the first rope?

## 41

If a post is 6 yards longer than half of its own length, how long is the post?

## 42

How much mud (measured in liters) is there in a rectangular hole 2 meters wide, 3 meters long, and 3 meters deep?

## 43

One mother gave 25 books to her daughter and another mother gave her daughter 8 books. However, between both daughters they only increased their collection by 25 books. How can this be?

## COMPARING TIME, VOLUME, LENGTH, ETC.

### 44

Emily is taller than Ann and shorter than Dolores. Who is the tallest of the three?

### 45

Rose is now as old as Joan was six years ago. Who is older?

### 46

If Emily speaks in a softer voice than Ann, and Dolores in a louder voice than Ann, does Emily speak louder or softer than Dolores?

### 47

James is sitting between John and Peter. Philip is sitting on Peter's right. Between whom is Peter sitting?

## 48

What has more value, one pound of $10 gold coins or half a pound of $20 gold coins?

## 49

A man went into a store and bought an umbrella for $10. He gave the salesperson a $50 bill. The salesperson went to the bank to get change. Two hours later, the bank teller went to the store claiming that the $50 bill was counterfeit, so the salesperson had to exchange it for a real one with the bank teller. Between the customer and the bank, how much did the store lose?

## 50

We have two pitchers, one with one quart of water and the other with one quart of wine. We take a tablespoon of the wine and mix it in the pitcher of water. Then we take a tablespoon from this pitcher and mix it into the pitcher with the wine. Is there more wine in the water pitcher or more water in the wine pitcher? What would have happened if after pouring a spoonful of wine into the water, we had not mixed it well?

# 51

A sultan wanted to offer his daughter in marriage to the candidate whose horse would win the race. However, the rules of the race stated that the winner would be the one in last place. He didn't want the race to last forever, so he thought of a way to solve this. What was it?

## WEIGHTS

# 52

On one side of a scale we have a partially filled fish bowl. When we put a fish in the bowl, the total weight of the bowl increases by exactly the same as the weight of the fish. However, if we hold the fish by the tail and partially introduce it into the water, will the total weight be greater than before introducing the fish?

# 53

We have a scale and a set of weights in a field. The scale is not very accurate, but it is consistent in its inaccuracies. How can we know the exact weight of four apples?

## 54

A little bird weighing 5 ounces is sleeping in a cage. We put the cage on a scale and it weighs one pound. The bird then wakes up and starts flying all over the cage. What will the scale indicate while the bird is in the air?

## 55

We have 10 sacks full of balls. All sacks contain balls weighing 10 ounces each, except one of the sacks, which contains balls weighing 9 ounces each. By weighing the balls, what would be the minimum number of weighings required (on a scale that gives weight readouts) to identify the sack containing the defective balls?

## 56

Now we have 10 sacks that contain either 10-ounce balls or 9-ounce balls. Each sack has at least 1,000 balls, and all the balls in one sack are the same weight. However, we do not know how many sacks contain the 9-ounce balls or which ones they are. How can we identify these sacks by weighing the balls (on a scale that gives weight readouts) in the fewest number of tries?

# CHAINS

## 57

I have six pieces of a chain, each piece made up of 4 links, and I want to make a single straight chain out of them. The blacksmith charges 10 cents for cutting each link and 50 cents for welding a link. How much will the chain cost?

## 58

A lady arrives at a hotel where rooms are $10 per night. When she checks in, she does not have enough money, but she offers to pay with a clasped gold bracelet. The bracelet has seven links, each valued at $10. What would be the fewest number of cuts necessary to let her stay for one week if she wants to pay one day at a time?

## 59

"And then I took out my sword and cut the thick chain that was linked to two posts into two pieces," said the samurai.

"That is not true," said the monk.

How did the monk know the samurai's story was untrue?

# MIXING

## 60

We have 10 glasses sitting in a row. The first five are filled with water and the other five are empty. What would be the minimum number of glasses needed to move so that the full and the empty glasses alternate?

## 61

In five plastic cups there are five marbles, each of different colors: white, black, red, green, and blue. We mark each cup randomly with the initial of one of the colors. If the white, green, red, and blue marbles are in their respective cups, how likely is it that the black marble is in its cup?

## 62

We have 8 pairs of white socks and 10 pairs of black socks in a box. What would be the minimum number of socks that we need to take out of the box to ensure that we get one pair of the same color? (Imagine that you cannot see the color when you are picking them from the box.)

## 63

We have 8 pairs of white socks, 9 pairs of black socks and 11 pairs of blue socks in a box. What would be the minimum number of socks that we need to take out of the box to ensure that we get one pair of the same color? (Imagine that you cannot see the color when you are picking them from the box.)

## 64

We have 6 pairs of white gloves and 6 pairs of black gloves in a box. What would be the minimum number of gloves that we need to take out of the box to ensure that we get one pair? (Imagine that you cannot see the color when you are picking them from the box.)

## 65

We have six white marbles, four black marbles, and one red marble in a box. What would be the least number of marbles that we need to take out of the box to ensure that we get three of the same color?

## 66

Distribute ten marbles in three plastic cups so that every cup contains an odd number of marbles. You must use all ten.

## 67

Distribute nine marbles in four boxes so that each box contains an odd number of marbles, different from the three other boxes. You must use all nine.

## 68

We have three boxes. One contains two black marbles, the second box contains two white marbles, and the third box contains one black and one white marble. The boxes are marked BB, WW, BW. However, no code corresponds with the marbles in its box. What would be the least number of marbles that must be randomly picked, from one or several boxes, to identify their contents?

## CLOCKS

## 69

A schoolteacher uses a five-hour hourglass to keep track of class time. One day, he sets the hourglass at 9 a.m. and while he is teaching his class, a student inadvertently inverts the hourglass. Another student, who notices this, sets the hourglass to its initial position at 11:30 a.m. In this way, the class ends at 3 p.m. At what time did the first student invert the hourglass?

## 70

A clock gains half a minute every day. Another clock doesn't work. Which one will show the correct time more often?

## 71

What time is it when a clock strikes 13 times?

## 72

In a conventional clock, how many times does the minute hand pass the hour hand between noon and midnight?

## 73

If a clock takes two seconds to strike 2, how long will it take to strike 3?

## 74

When I gave Albert a ride home, I noticed that the clock in his living room took 7 seconds to strike 8. I immediately asked him, "How long do I have to wait to hear it strike 12?"

## 75

A clock takes five seconds when striking 6. How long will it take when striking 12?

## CALENDAR

## 76

A Roman was born the first day of the 30th year before Christ and died the first day of the 30th year after Christ. How many years did he live?

## 77

On March 15, a friend was telling me, "Every day I have a cup of coffee. I drank 31 cups in January, 28 in February and 15 in March.

So far, I drank 74 cups of coffee. Do you know how many cups I would have drunk thus far if it had been a leap year?"

## 78

If yesterday had been Wednesday's tomorrow and tomorrow is Sunday's yesterday, what day would today be?

## 79

Mrs. Smith left on a trip the day after the day before yesterday and she will be back the eve of the day after tomorrow. How many days is she away?

## 80

A man was telling me on a particular occasion, "The day before yesterday I was 35 years old and next year I will turn 38." How can this be?

## 81

A famous composer blew out 18 candles on his birthday cake and then died less than nine months later. He was 76 at the time of his death and had composed *The Barber of Seville*. How could this happen?

## 82

Find a commonly used word that ends in T, contains the letters VEN, and starts with IN.

## 83

If you can speak properly, you will be able to answer the following question. Which is correct, "The yolk of an egg is white" or "The yolk of an egg are white"?

## 84

What is the opposite of "I AM NOT LEAVING"?

## 85

What 11-letter word is pronounced incorrectly by more than 99% of Ivy League graduates?

## 86

What 7-letter word becomes longer when the third letter is removed?

## 87

Five times four twenty, plus two, equals twenty-three. Is this true?

## 88

Paris starts with an "p" and ends with an "e." Is this true?

## 89

A phone conversation:
    "May I speak to the director?"
    "Who's calling?"
    "John Rominch."
    "I beg your pardon. Could you spell your last name?"
    "R as in Rome, O as in Oslo, M as in Madrid, I as in Innsbruck ..."
    "I as in what?"
    "Innsbruck."
    "Thanks. Please go ahead."
    "N as in Nome ..."
This does not make sense. Why?

## 90

What can you always find in the middle of a taxicab?

## 91

Is the sentence "This statement is false" true or false?

## 92

What occurs once in June and twice in August, but never occurs in October?

## 93

"I must admit that I was not serious when I was telling you that I was not kidding about rethinking my decision of not changing my mind," my friend was telling me. So, is he really going to change his mind or not?

## 94

A criminal is sentenced to death. Before his execution, he is allowed to make a statement. If his statement is false, he will be hanged, and if his statement is true, he will be drowned. What should he say to confuse the jury and thus save his life?

## COUNTING RELATIVES

## 95

A woman has five children and half of them are male. Is this possible?

## 96

A friend was telling me, "I have eight sons and each has one sister." In total, how many children does my friend have?

## 97

Ann's brother has one more brother than sisters. How many more brothers than sisters does Ann have?

## 98

"I have as many brothers as sisters, but my brothers have twice the number of sisters as brothers. How many of us are there?"

## FAMILY TIES

## 99

A doctor has a brother who is an attorney in Alabama, but the attorney in Alabama does not have a brother who is a doctor. How can this be?

## 100

John wonders, "If Raymond's son is my son's father, how am I related to Raymond?"

## 101

If your uncle's sister is related to you, but is not your aunt, what is the relation?

## 102

A group of paleontologists found a prehistoric cave and one of them is congratulated by a younger son, who writes a telegram to his dad explaining the discovery. Who discovered the cave?

## 103

The other day, I heard the following conversation:
"Charles is related to you the same way I am to your son."
"And you are related to me in the same way Charles is to you."
How are Charles and the second man related?

## 104

Can someone marry his brother's wife's mother-in-law?

## 105

Ann is looking at the portrait of a gentleman. "He is not my father, but his mother was my mother's mother-in-law," she says. Who is this gentleman?

## 106

Do you know if the Catholic Church allows a man to marry his widow's sister?

## 107

A friend of mine was looking at a photo when she said, "Brothers and sisters? I have one. And this man's father is my father's son." Who was in the photo?

## 108

A friend of mine was looking at a photo when he said, "Brother and sisters? I have none. But this man's son is my father's son." Who was in the photo?

## 109

Two women are talking on the street. When they see two men coming, they say, "There are our fathers, our mothers' husbands, our children's fathers, and our own husbands." How can you explain this?

## 110

What was the biggest ocean in the world before Balboa discovered the Pacific Ocean?

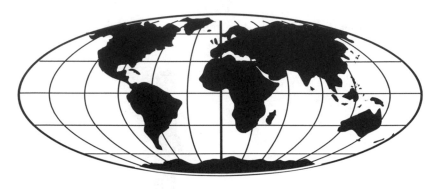

## 111

How many cookies could you eat on an empty stomach?

## 112

Three mature and hefty women were walking in San Francisco under one regular-size umbrella. Why didn't they get wet?

## 113

What can a pitcher be filled with so it is lighter than when it is full of air?

## 114

A dog is tied to a 15-foot long leash. How can the dog reach a bone that is 20 feet away?

## 115

I went into a store and found out that it cost $3 for 400, which meant that each part cost $1. What did I want to buy?

# 116

Last week, my uncle Peter was able to turn his bedroom light off and get into bed before the room was dark. The light switch and the bed are ten feet apart. How did he accomplish this?

# 117

How can you make 30 cents with only two coins if one of the coins is not a nickel?

# 118

The only barber in my town likes foreigners to go into his shop. Last week, he was telling me, "The truth is that I'd rather give two foreigners haircuts than to give a haircut to one person in town." What was the logic behind this?

# 119

My brother Mark says he is able to place a bottle in the middle of a room and by crawling on the floor, he can slide into it. How can this be?

# 120

Last Friday I flew to San Diego. It was a scary flight. About an hour after getting onto the plane, I saw a very thick fog and then the engines stopped due to lack of fuel. Why didn't we die?

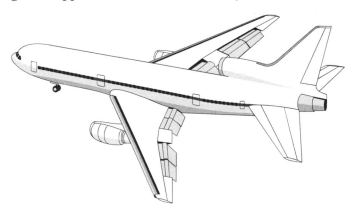

## 121

While eating out, my brother-in-law Paul found a fly in his coffee. After taking the cup away, the waiter came back with a different cup of coffee. My brother-in-law got upset and returned it, saying that the coffee in the second cup was the same as in the first one. How did he know?

## 122

You find shelter in a mountain lodge on a windy night. When you go in, you only find a match, a candle, a sheet of newspaper, and a torch. You need to light the fireplace. What would you light first?

## 123

A mother has six children and five potatoes. How can she feed each an equal amount of potatoes? (Do not use fractions.)

## 124

The giraffe and its offspring are walking in a field. The little giraffe tells a friend, "I am the daughter of this giraffe, although this giraffe is not my mother." How can you explain this?

## 125

A farmer has twenty sheep, ten pigs, and ten cows. If we call the pigs cows, how many cows will he have?

## 126

Where must a referee be to blow the whistle?

## 127

In the event of an emergency, can a Muslim baptize a Catholic?

## 128

It occurs once in a minute, twice in a week, and once in a year. What is it?

## 129

One night, when my uncle Emil was reading a book in the living room, his wife turned off the light and the living room became completely dark. However, my uncle continued reading. How is this possible?

## 130

A man says, "I am going to drink water because I don't have water. If I had it, I would drink wine." What does he do for a living?

## 131

Imagine you are a taxi driver and you are driving a 1978 yellow cab. Your passengers are an older couple, and they want to travel 6 miles. You are driving at 40 miles per hour with the tank one-third full, when, 2 miles into the trip, the tank is down to one-quarter full. Ten minutes later, the trip is over. What is the name and age of the cab driver?

## 132

A railway line has a double track, except in a tunnel where there was no room for a double track. A train goes into the tunnel in one direction, and another one enters in the opposite direction. Both trains are traveling fast. However, they do not crash. Why?

## 133

My son was telling me yesterday, "Four days ago, my school's soccer team won a game 4 to 1, although none of the boys on my school's team scored any goals. Also, the other team didn't score against itself accidentally." How can this be?

## 134

Last Thursday, my aunt Martha forgot her driver's license at home. She was traveling down a one way street in the wrong direction and did not stop at an intersection to let pedestrians go. A policeman was watching her, but did not give her a ticket. Why?

## 135

Three friends went out for drinks. The waiter brought them a check for $30, so each one of them paid $10. When the waiter took the cash, he realized he had made a mistake, and the check was for $25 instead. When he gave their change back, each friend got a dollar and they left the remaining two dollars as a tip. Therefore, each customer paid $9; multiplied by 3 this equals $27; plus $2 for the tip equals $29. Where is the remaining dollar?

## 136

A 16-year-old boy was driving a moped down a one-way street in the wrong direction. A policeman stopped him and gave him a ticket. The policeman paid the ticket himself. Can you find a logical explanation for this?

## 137

The butcher, his daughter, the fisherman, and his wife won the lottery and divided the prize into three. How can this be?

## 138

My friend Albert the butcher wears a size 13 shoe, is six feet tall, and wears a 42-long suit. What does he weigh?

## 139

There are five apples in one basket and five people in a room. How can you distribute the apples so that each person receives one and there is one apple left in the basket?

## 140

A man is doing his work. He knows that if his suit tears, he will die. Can you guess his job?

## 141

We have just invented two words: to sint and to sant. You cannot sint or sant in the street or in the office. You can do both things in the bathroom, the swimming pool, and the beach, but in the swimming pool and the beach you cannot sint completely. You cannot sint without clothes on and you need little or no clothing to sant. Can you guess what the words mean?

## 142

My cousin Henry can guess the score of a soccer game before the game begins. How can that be?

## 143

Before my husband left on a trip, he left me $150 in cash and a $500 check. However, when I went to the bank to cash the check, I found out that the account only had $450. How could I cash the check?

## 144

A bus stops three times during the ride. The ticket costs 12 cents to the first stop, 21 to the second stop, and 25 to the third stop. A man gets on at the start of the route and gives the driver 25 cents. Without talking to the passenger, the driver gives him a ticket to the last stop. How did the driver know?

## 145

You've probably heard the expression "two's company and three's a crowd." But what's the simplest way to describe four and five?

## 146

Mary, riding her white horse, decides to go into the forest. How far can she go?

## 147
What animal eats with its tail?

## 148
How can you light a match under water?

## 149
What three shapes can a saber have for it to fit in a sheath?

## 150
"This parrot can repeat anything it hears," the owner of the pet shop told Janice last week. So my sister bought it. Yesterday, she went to return it, claiming that the parrot had not even said one word. However, the pet shop owner had not lied to her. Can you explain this?

## 151
A man and his son were in a car accident. The boy had a fracture and injuries to one leg and was taken to a nearby hospital in an ambulance. When he was in the operating room, the surgeon said, "I cannot operate on him! He is my son!" Explain this.

## 152
Why do black sheep eat less grass than white sheep?

## 153

My cousin Mary dropped an earring in her coffee, but the earring did not get wet. How could this be?

## 154

I have a book where the foreword comes after the epilogue, the end is in the first half of the book, and the index comes before the introduction. What book is it?

## 155

How can you explain that one lady works alone as a bartender, yet there is a COUPLE that works behind the counter?

## 156

My uncle Raphael bought a coin in the flea market for 10 dollars. The coin has the head of Emperor Augustus and is dated 27 b.c. The other side is illegible. It is a fake, however. What proves that it is not a true ancient Roman coin?

## 157

An Air France plane crashes along the border of Portugal and Spain. Rescue teams from both countries are called to the site of the crash to help the victims. In which country do you think the survivors will be buried?

## 158

The director of a large company asks the security guard working the night shift to call him a cab, because he needs to take a red-eye flight to New York. The guard tells him not to board the plane, because he had just had a dream that the director would have an accident. To be safe, the director decides to wait until the next morning. During the trip, he reads in the paper that the red-eye flight had crashed. When he returns from his trip, he thanks the guard and gives him a bonus. Then he fires him. Why did he fire him?

## 159

My cousin Edward got soaked while he was walking on the street yesterday. He did not have an umbrella or a hat, so when he got home, his clothes were completely wet. However, not a hair on his head got wet. Why?

## 160

My sister Sophie lives on the 28th floor of a 32-story building. When my aunt Emily visits her, she takes the elevator to the 25th floor and then walks up the stairs. On her way down, she takes the elevator at the 28th floor all the way down to the ground floor. Why does she do this?

## 161

A man was sleeping in a hotel. In the middle of the night, he woke up and could not go back to sleep. He picked up the phone and called someone. As soon as he hung up, he fell sound asleep. He did not know the person he was calling. Why did he call that person?

## 162

When he goes to the bathroom, a man does not know if the hot water faucet is the one on the left or on the right. What does he need to do to be sure that he does not turn on the cold water before he turns on the hot water?

## 163

A man took his wife to the emergency room. The doctor decided to operate on her immediately. He told the husband that whether the wife died during the operation or survived, he would charge $1,000. The woman did not survive the operation. The husband did not pay anything. Why not?

## 164

The brothers Albert, Ben, Carl, and Don wear shirt sizes 37, 38, 39, and 40, respectively. Their mother bought one blue shirt for each one of them and embroidered their first initials on the left side. She placed three initials correctly. How many different ways can this happen?

## 165

If the date of the last Saturday of last month and the first Sunday of this month do not add up to 33, what month are we in?

## 166

The priest in my hometown announced last year that on a particular day he would walk on water for half an hour. The river was not dry and we could all see that the priest was actually able to walk on water. How did he manage?

## 167

Two miners go home after work. One of them has his face covered with soot and the other has a clean face. The one with a clean face wipes it with a handkerchief and the one with the dirty face does not do anything. Why?

## 168

What is there in the middle of a cigar?

## 169

A remote town has two hair salons. The first one has a dirty mirror, a floor covered with hair, and the hairdresser has an awful haircut. In the second one, the mirror and floor are very clean and the hairdresser has a great haircut. Where would you go and why?

## 170

A man ordered a glass of white wine and a glass of red wine at a bar. He took the glass of white wine in his right hand and the one with red in his left hand and drank both. He paid and left. The next day, he did the same. When he was leaving, the waiter asked him:

"I did not know that firemen drank that way."

The man smiled and left. How did the waiter know that he was a fireman?

## 171

Three meteorologists left a meeting in the middle of the night, during a heavy rain.

"The weather will remain like this until the next full moon," said one of them.

"I agree. And 96 hours from now, the sun will not shine," said the second one.

"I agree more with you than with the first forecast," said the third one.

Why was the third meteorologist so sure?

## 172

A criminal took his wife to the movies to watch a western. During a gunshot scene, he killed his wife with a bullet to her heart. When he left the movies with his wife's dead body, nobody tried to stop him. How did he manage this?

## 173

In the 5th century a.d. a king was taking his daily bath when he received a huge crown that he had ordered made from one of his bars of gold. He knew that the crown and the gold weighed the same, although he suspected that part of the gold had been replaced with lighter materials, such as copper or silver. How did he find out quickly?

## 174

If I take two apples out of a basket containing six apples, how many apples do I have?

## 175

How much will a 38° angle measure when observed under a microscope that magnifies ten times?

## 176

John Peterson was born in Albany in 1938, on a date not divisible by 2, 3, or 5, and in a month that does not contain the letters "e" or "i." When does he become one year older?

## 177

A passenger traveling by bus between Springfield and Capital City noticed that, due to the heavy traffic, it took him 80 minutes to reach his destination at an average speed of 40 mph. On his return trip, he took the bus and it took him 1 hour and 20 minutes at the same average speed and with less traffic. Do you know why?

## 178

A man traveling in a taxi is talking to the driver. After a while, the driver tells him, "You must excuse me, but I am deaf and cannot hear a word of what you are saying." The passenger stops talking. After he gets out of the cab, the passenger realizes that the driver had lied to him. How?

## 179

My friend told me the following story: "I was drinking a Coke in a bar when a man wearing a mustache came in and ordered a glass of water. As the waiter came back with his water, he pointed a gun at the customer. The customer got startled, but then calmed down and thanked the waiter." How can you explain what happened?

## 180

A 30-year-old man married a 25-year-old woman. She died at the age of 50 and her husband was so devastated that he cried for years. Ten years after he stopped crying, he died. However, he lived to be 80. How many years was he a widower?

## 181

Two rich men, now bankrupt, came across each other one day. After exchanging greetings and catching up with what had happened in their lives, they compared how much money each had. The first one had 80 dollars and the second one had only 42 dollars. However, two hours later, between both of them they had more than 84 million dollars in cash. None of them had inherited anything, won the lottery, or received payment for a debt or loan. How could this be?

## 182

I am sitting at a table. Ten flies are on the table. With one swat, I kill three flies. How many flies are left on the table?

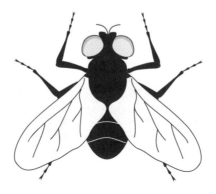

# INTELLIGENCE AND SKILLS

## 183

How can you drop a matchbook match from five feet above the ground so that it comes to rest with one of its thin edges touching the ground?

## 184

How can you drop an egg a distance of three feet without breaking it?

## 185

How can you divide a round pie in eight equal pieces by cutting only three straight lines?

## 186

Two thin ropes hang from the high ceiling of an empty room, just too far apart from each other to be grabbed with both hands at the same time. How can you tie a knot with both rope ends using only a pair of sharp scissors?

## 187

A sparrow has fallen into a hole in a rock. The hole measures three inches in diameter and is three feet deep. Due to the depth of the hole, the sparrow cannot be reached by hand. We cannot use sticks or canes, because we could hurt the bird. How can you get the bird out?

## 188

A homeless man runs out of cigarettes. He looks for cigarette butts since he knows that he can make one new cigarette out of every three butts. He picks up nine butts. If he smokes one cigarette per hour, how many hours can he smoke for?

## 189

How can you make a hole in a paper napkin and then fit your body through it without tearing the napkin?

## 190

How can you form four equilateral triangles with six toothpicks of equal length?

## 191

You go on a picnic with your friends. Each one of them wants a different amount of oil and vinegar in his salad. However, you've already mixed the oil and vinegar in one bottle. How can you please everyone at the picnic?

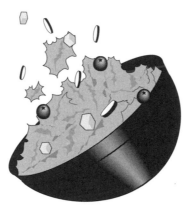

## 192

The maximum length of a postal package is 30 inches. How can you mail an iron bar that measures 40 inches in length without bending it?

## 193

How can you tie a knot with a napkin by holding one end in each hand without letting go of it?

## 194

If you cut a circle the size of a nickel in a piece of paper, can you pass a silver dollar through it?

## 195

A six-foot long rope is tied to a hook fixed to the ceiling of a room. We tie a mug by the handle to the loose end of the rope. If you cut the rope in half, how can you prevent the mug from falling? (There is nothing between the floor and the mug. Nobody is holding on to the mug.)

## 196

Two thick ropes hang from a high ceiling attached to hooks three feet apart. The ends touch the ground. Without using anything else, and considering that you will die if you fall from one-quarter of the height of the room, how can you cut the largest amount possible of each rope with a knife?

## 197

You are playing table tennis on the beach when your only ball falls into a hole in the sand that someone else had used for their beach umbrella. The hole is only slightly larger in diameter than the ball. How can you take the ball out without digging?

## 198

A truck is about to go under a bridge, although its load is two inches higher than the clearance of the bridge. It is a very heavy load, so it cannot be unloaded. How can it pass under the bridge in a quick and simple way?

## 199

How could you throw a tennis ball so that after traveling a short distance, it stops and returns following the same path? The ball cannot hit or be tied to anything.

## 200

A brick measuring 5 centimeters high, 20 centimeters long, and 10 centimeters wide falls off a dike causing a leak that must be stopped immediately. How can you stop the leak with a saw and a wooden cylinder measuring 5 centimeters in diameter?

## 201

With your pants on, can you put your right hand in your left pocket and your left hand in your right pocket?

## 202

I bet that you alone cannot take off your left shoe using only your right hand. I will not touch you or interfere with your movements. How can I prevent this?

## 203

How can you pour wine out of a corked bottle that is half full without breaking or damaging the bottle or the cork, and without taking out the cork?

## 204

You keep some of your diamonds in a jewelry case with a sliding cover. To keep thieves away, you put a scorpion inside the case. One day you need to take some of the diamonds. How can you do it without taking the scorpion out, while protecting your hands from its bites, only taking a few seconds, and leaving the case in the same way you originally had it?

## 205

I am going to make you a bet: "On this folded piece of paper I have written down the prediction of something that might or might not happen in the next five minutes. Put it in your pocket. On this blank piece of paper, write "YES" if you think that it will happen and "NO" if you think it will not happen. I'll bet you a cup of coffee that you cannot guess right." What have I written on the paper? (It is something that can be proven.)

## 206

Your rich relative gathers the family together to tell them, "I will leave my inheritance to the one who can collect the exact number of pennies equaling half the number of days that I have left to live." What would you do to inherit the fortune?

## 207

How can two people step on one page of newspaper so that they can't touch each other without stepping off the newspaper?

## 208

A friend told me, "I can do something that you are not able to, no matter how hard you try." What could it be?

## 209

A bottle is standing on a rug (or upside down on a dollar bill). Can you take out the rug or the bill without turning or touching the bottle and without help from anybody else?

## 210

Set an imaginary finish line somewhere (for example, a point on the wall 10 feet away from you). Find a method of advancing so that even though you always move ahead, you never reach the finish line.

## 211

Yesterday, someone dared me to jump over a ballpoint pen on the floor. I could not, even though I'm a good jumper. How come I wasn't able to?

# INVESTIGATIONS AND TRIALS

## 212

A plane was hijacked. The hijacker demanded two parachutes and ten million dollars. Once he got both, he jumped off the plane during the night and while in flight. Why did he need two parachutes?

## 213

One rainy day, my cousin Ernest found a dead body lying next to a strange package. He could not see any footprints in the area.

Because of the temperature of the body, Ernest knew that the man had been dead for less than one hour. What was in the package? How did the man get there?

## 214

A man walking along a rural road was being sought by the police. When he saw a patrol car approaching him, he thought of running toward the forest. Instead, he ran 20 yards toward the approaching car. Why?

## 215

Stella was telling my cousin Ernest that her husband once fell asleep in the opera and started dreaming of being on a plane that was hijacked. The hijacker demanded to fly to an African country. People complained, screamed, and fainted. The hijacker was pointing a gun to Stella's husband's head. At this point, the husband started to move and make noise. Stella tapped her husband on the shoulder and he got so startled that he fell on the floor and died from the impact. Ernest immediately said, "This story is impossible." How did he know?

# 216

My cousin Ernest solved this case. A man was hanged, his feet half a meter above the ground, in the middle of a very hot room, hanging by a rope tied to a hook from the ceiling. The room was completely empty and had some moisture on the floor. On the other side of the door there was a ladder, which must have been used by the victim. However, the investigation proved that the victim had no place to lean the ladder against to reach the rope. That is how Ernest realized that this was not a murder, but a suicide. How could it have happened?

# 217

Last winter, my cousin Ernest went on a ski vacation. At the airport, he read in the papers that a famous couple had been skiing and the wife had died in an accident. Her well-known husband was the only eyewitness. After talking to a travel agent, my cousin was able to deduce that it had not been an accident. What did he find out from the travel agent?

# 218

A medieval count organized a court trial in which he gave the defendant a chance to save his life if he could pick a white marble out of a bag containing, in the count's words, one white marble and one black marble. The accused knew that this was a trick, because he had seen the count place two black marbles in the bag. However, he went ahead and took out a marble. What did he do to save his life?

# 219

During the war, my cousin Ernest was captured and put into a prison cell. It was in the basement, with a dirt floor, armored walls, and a water tank 10 feet from the ground. There was no furniture and no object to reach the water tank with. How did Ernest manage to drink?

## 220

My cousin Ernest, amateur private investigator, was able to figure out the weapon used in a suicide case. The man had been stabbed, but the weapon was nowhere in the room. The room was locked from the inside. The deceased had the only key. During the investigation, they found out that the weapon had been thicker than typical knives. What was the weapon? Where was it?

## 221

When Ernest went to visit his friend Albert, he found him dead on his desk with a bullet through the head. He saw a cassette player and decided to listen to the tape. He hit play and heard, "This is Albert. I just got a call saying that someone is on his way here to kill me and that he will be here in less than three minutes. I hear steps. Someone is opening the door." At that point, my cousin knew that it was not Albert's voice on the tape, but the killer's. How did he know that?

## 222

A man has been killed in a room locked from the inside with a vertical deadbolt. The killer was able to lock it from the outside. How did he do this?

## 223

A businessman was working in his home office when he realized he had left a five-dollar bill in the book he had been reading. He called his butler to bring him the book from the library. When he got the book, the bill was no longer there. He then questioned the maid and the butler. The maid remembered seeing the bill between pages 99 and 100 in a book to the left of a business book. The butler did not recall seeing the bill, but was sure the book was to the right of the business book, because to the left of it there was a statistics book.

Who is lying?

## 224

On the 29th of last month, there was a double murder on the express train from Paris to Berlin. The driver and the conductor were killed at the same time, even though they were at opposite ends of the train. This was confirmed by a police detective, who was at the exact center of the train and heard both gunshots at the same time.

When my cousin was told this story, he realized that both victims did not die at the same time.

How did he figure it out?

## 225

Two people were accused of murder. In a court trial, one had been acquitted and the other had been found guilty. When the judge had to sentence the guilty man, he said, "This is the strangest case that I have ever presided over. Even though you have been found guilty, the law obliges me to set you free." Can you explain this?

## 226

My cousin Ernest was once kidnapped. He knew they would either take him to New York City or to Sydney, Australia. When they took his blindfold off, he could see he had been locked in a room without windows. There was only a table, a bed, a chair, and a sink. However, Ernest was able to figure out which city he was in. How did he do it?

## 227

These are the clues to a robbery and murder on a ground floor office:
- A. The killer had to be one of these three people: the muscly engineer, the obese director, or the perky secretary.
- B. The stolen goods were taken out from the open window. There were light footprints under it in the snow.
- C. The footprints matched the director's shoes, which were found next to the crime weapon.
- D. Only one bullet was found, although there were two wounds to the body, one to the chest and the other to the right hand.

Who was the killer? Why were there two wounds?

# RIDDLES

## 228

I climbed up a cherry tree, where I found cherries. I did not pick cherries, nor did I leave cherries. How can you explain this?

## 229

What animal walks on all fours in the morning, on two legs at noon, and on three legs at dusk?

## 230

What is so fragile that when you say its name you break it?

### 231

Among my siblings I am the thinnest. I am in Paris, but I am not in France. Who am I?

### 232

I can only live when there is light, although I die if the light shines on me. What am I?

## ELEMENTS IN MOVEMENT

### 233

A ship is anchored offshore. In order for the crew to reach the rafts, they must descend a 22-step ladder. Each step is 10 inches high. The tide rises at a ratio of 5 inches per hour. How many steps will the tide have covered after 10 hours?

### 234

A 100-meter long train moving 100 meters per minute must pass through a tunnel of 100 meters in length. How long will it take?

### 235

A train headed for Barcelona leaves Madrid at midnight, at a constant speed of 60 kilometers per hour. Another train leaves Barcelona at the same time, heading for Madrid at a constant speed of 40 kilometers per hour. The distance between both cities is 600 kilometers. The train that left from Madrid stops for half an hour when both trains cross. Which train was closer to Madrid when they crossed?

## 236

My uncle Lou takes the subway to the movies or the theater every evening. He always takes the first subway that stops at the station close to his home, no matter which direction it is heading. If the subway is heading north, he will go to the theater. If it is heading south, he will go to the movies. Both trains run every 10 minutes. However, nine times out of every ten, my uncle ends up at the movies. How can you explain this?

## 237

A cyclist takes 2 minutes and 13 seconds for every full lap of a circuit. Answer in 10 seconds: How long will he take to do 60 laps?

## 238

My bird can fly faster than any airplane. How can this be?

## 239

Albert, who was just back from his trip around the world in a sailboat, asked me, "What part of my boat has traveled the longest distance?"

Do you know the answer to that?

## 240

If we tie a light oxygen tank to a bird so that it can breathe on the moon, would the bird fly faster, slower, or the same speed as it does on earth? (Remember that there is less gravity on the moon.)

## 241

What can a train passenger do to be in a tunnel the least time possible while the train is going through a 100-meter long tunnel?

## 242

Two trains travel on parallel tracks in opposite directions, at 70 and 50 miles per hour. When the trains are 60 miles apart, a bird flying at 80 miles per hour leaves the first train and flies off to the second. It keeps on flying back and forth until both trains cross. How many miles does the bird fly?

## 243

We drag a large stone over three logs measuring 50 inches in circumference each. What distance does the stone cover each time the logs make one rotation?

## 244

Two trains are moving on the same track in opposite directions. One goes 80 meters per minute and the other 120 meters per minute. After 12 hours, they are 1700 meters apart. How far apart will they be one minute before they collide?

## 245

A snail is climbing up a one-meter high wall. It advances three centimeters per minute and then stops for one minute to rest, during which it slides back down two centimeters. How long will the snail take to reach the top of the wall?

## 246

A young man gets on the end car of a train. Just as the train passes by Cat City, he leaves his suitcases and walks at a steady pace to find a seat. After five minutes, he reaches the front car. Not finding a seat, he returns at the same pace to where his luggage is. At that point, the train passes by Dog City, which is five miles from Cat City. How fast is the train going?

## 247

A journey by ship between New York and London takes seven days. Ships leave from both ports at the same time every day. During a trip, how many other ships will a ship come across?

## 248

A regular LP record measures 30 centimeters in diameter. The outer blank (non-recorded) area is 5 millimeters in width. The non-playable center area measures 10 centimeters in diameter. The grooves are ¼ millimeter apart. What is the distance traveled by the needle during the time that the record is playing?

## 249

A man is walking at night at a steady pace. As he passes by a street lamp, he notices that his shadow becomes longer. Does the top of the shadow move faster, slower, or the same when the shadow is longer as when it is shorter?

## 250

A kid who is in the back seat of a car is holding the string of a helium balloon. The balloon is floating without touching the roof of the car, and the windows are closed. When the car accelerates, where does the balloon go? And when the car turns, where does it go?

## 251

A train goes from north to south, although at all times there are certain areas of the train that are moving in a south-to-north direction. What are these areas?

## 252

A railway track measures 5 kilometers in length and its ties are one meter apart. A child ties a can to a dog's tail. As the dog starts running along the tracks, it increases its speed by one meter per second every time it hears the noise of the can hitting a tie. If the dog starts to run at a speed of 1 meter/second and the can hits all of the railway ties, what is the dog's speed at the end of the track?

## 253

Two athletes ran in a 100-meter race. When the runner with the number "1" on his jersey reached the finish line, the runner with number "2" had only run 95 meters. In a second race, the number "1" runner had to start 5 meters behind the start line. If both ran at the same speed as in the first race, who won this time?

## 254

A driver always leaves the office at the same time, gets to the director's house at the same time, picks him up, and takes him to the office. One morning, the director decides to leave one hour earlier and he starts walking to the office along his usual route. When he sees the car, he gets in and continues his trip. He reaches the office 20 minutes earlier than usual. How long was he walking for?

## 255

In a river without a current, a ship leaves from a certain point, goes three miles up the river, turns around and goes back to the point of departure in 20 minutes. If the river has a current of two miles per hour and the ship did the same trip at the same speed (with respect to the water), would the trip last more or less than 20 minutes?

## 256

A mountaineer starts rapidly climbing up a mountain trail at 6 a.m. He makes frequent and irregular stops to rest or eat. He reaches the summit at 6 p.m. At 6 a.m. the next day, he starts his way back following the same route, stopping only once to eat. He reaches the starting point at 6 p.m. Is there a point on the way where he passes at exactly the same time on both days?

## 257

Which is warmer, a two-inch thick blanket or two blankets one inch thick each?

## 258

Three ice cubes are melting in a glass of water. Once they have completely melted, has the water level of the glass changed?

## 259

A super-accurate bomb, one that always hits the bull's-eye and destroys it, hits an indestructible fort. What will happen?

## 260

A man gets up 180 times every night and sleeps for at least 7 hours at a stretch. Where does he live?

## 261

I had just made myself a cup of coffee when I realized I had to run upstairs for a moment. I did not want the coffee to get cold, and I had to add milk at room temperature. Should I add the milk before I go up or after I get back?

## 262

A raft loaded with rocks is floating in a swimming pool. We mark the level of water in the swimming pool and on the raft. If we drop the rocks into the pool, what will happen to the water level in the pool and to the flotation line of the raft? Will they go up or down?

## 263

A boat is floating in a pool. We mark the flotation line. If we drop rocks into the pool and make the water level rise five inches, will the water rise more or less than five inches compared to the mark we made on the boat?

## 264

Two ivy branches sprout out of a tree trunk from the same point at ground level. One wraps around four times to the right, the other wraps around five times to the left, and their ends meet. Without counting the ends, how many times do both branches of ivy intersect?

## 265

An African trader is visiting different tribes in a raft loaded with sacks of salt, which he trades according to their weight in gold. When he is about to trade them, he realizes that the scale is broken. How can he trade the same weight of salt for gold?

# A LITTLE BIT OF EVERYTHING

## 266

We have a bottle of wine approximately three-fourths full. We want to leave an amount of wine in the bottle equal to exactly half of the total capacity of the bottle. How can we do it without using anything to help us?

## 267

We have three glass pitchers. One is a three-quart pitcher and is empty. The twelve-quart one is also empty. The third one is clear in color and irregular in shape. It contains acid. It has two marks, a two-quart mark and a five-quart mark. The level of acid is a little less than five quarts. We want to take out exactly three quarts of acid, but when we try it, the three-quart pitcher breaks. What can we do to take out the desired amount by pouring it into the twelve-quart pitcher, which is the only one left?

## 268

A man was used to walking at a regular pace. He never wore a watch, although he had a very accurate clock at home. One day, he forgot to wind it and the clock stopped. He went to a friend's house two miles from his home to ask the time. He spent the afternoon with him and when he came back home, he set the clock to the exact time. How did he know the exact time?

## 269

We have two similar coins and we make one spin on the edge of the other. How many times does the spinning coin turn on itself each time it makes an entire lap around the stationary one?

## 270

Mr. Brown, Mr. White, and Mr. Red are in a meeting. The three are wearing ties that are the three colors of their last names, although no man's tie matches his name. Mr. Brown asks the man with the white tie if he likes red, but cannot hear the answer. What is the color of each man's tie?

## 271

We mark three random points on a sphere. How likely are the three points to be in the same hemisphere?

## 272

Can you draw a square with two straight lines?

## LAUGHS

## 273

My cousin Henry can predict the future when he pets his black poodle. Is that possible?

## 274

An older woman and her young daughter, a young man, and an older man are traveling in the same compartment of a train. When the train passes through a tunnel, they hear a kiss and a slap. As the lights come back on, they can see the older man with a black eye. This is what each of the passengers thought:

The older woman: "He deserved it. I am glad my daughter can defend herself."

The daughter: "I cannot believe he preferred to kiss my mother or that young man over kissing me."

The older man: "What is going on here? I didn't do anything! Maybe the young man tried to kiss the girl, and she mistakenly slapped me."

The young man: "I know what really happened."

Do you know what happened?

## 275

An electric train runs at 60 mph heading south toward a wind blowing at 30 mph. What is the direction of the smoke from the train?

## 276

If Albert's peacock jumps over the fence onto Edward's property and lays an egg there, whose egg is it?

## 277

What can you have in an empty pocket? (Apart from air, of course.)

## 278

What did the twelve apostles make?

## 279

My cousin Herbert told me yesterday, "I can easily bite my eye." How can this be?

## 280

It sings and has ten feet. What is it?

## 281

Mary married John two years ago. She did not bring any money into the marriage and did not work during these two years, but she made her husband a millionaire. How did she do it?

## 282

My cousin Herbert told me this morning, "I can easily bite my good eye." How can he do this?

## 283

What can elephants make that no other animal can?

## 284

Last Thursday I walked back home from work (2 miles), and noticed a strange man following me the entire way. Once I got home, the man was still there walking around my building (a 100-by-100-yard square building). Later on, I saw he had fallen asleep next to the street lamp at the entrance of my building. During which lap did he fall asleep?

## 285

How can you get into your home if there is a dangerous dog inside that doesn't know you and belongs to your wife's friend?

## 286

A turtle, a gopher, and a hare are walking one behind the other in a straight line.

"I am first," said the turtle.

"I am second," said the gopher.

"I am first," said the hare.

How can you explain these statements?

## 287

What activity can only be done at night?

## 288

My cousin Robert was pushed into a well measuring six feet in diameter and 10 feet deep, with smooth walls and its bottom covered with water. How did he emerge from the well?

## 289

Every day, a cyclist crosses the border between Spain and France carrying a bag. No matter how much customs officials investigate him, they do not know what he is smuggling. Do you?

## 290

For the uninitiated, the next three puzzles are called cryptarithms or, more precisely, alphametics. Puzzle creator J. A. H. Hunter coined the term *alphametic* to designate words that have meaning, rather than the random use of letters found in cryptarithms.

The object of this type of puzzle is to replace letters with digits. Each letter must represent the same digit, and no beginning letter of a word can be zero. If properly constructed, alphametics can be deduced logically.

In the first puzzle, my verbal arithmetic leaves something to be desired. Assign a number to each letter to correct my addition. Hint: Make a box or chart to consider the possibilities of different values.

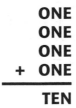

```
      ONE
      ONE
      ONE
  +   ONE
  ---------
      TEN
```

## 291

**NOON**
**MOON**
**+ SOON**

**JUNE**

## 292

This third alphametic is more difficult than the first two, and there is more than one correct answer. Hint: create more than one chart of values.

**THIS**
**IS**
**NOT**
**+ WITH**

**WHICH**

## 293

If B + P + F = 24, what are the values of Q and T? Hint: Consider whole numbers only.

$$A + B = Z$$
$$Z + P = T$$
$$T + A = F$$
$$F + S = Q$$
$$Q - T = 7$$

## 294

Here is a cube presented from five different perspectives. One of the views is incorrect. Can you tell which one?

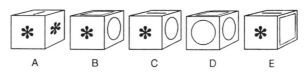

A     B     C     D     E

Here is one way to unfold the cube in puzzle 294.

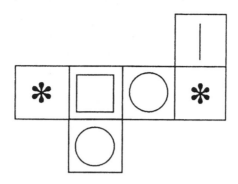

Here are two other ways to unfold a cube.
How many additional ways can a cube be unfolded?

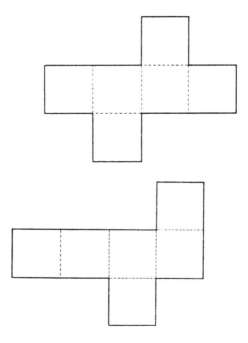

## 296

Your boss has asked you to purchase three different types of ballpoint pen. The first costs 50¢, the second $5.50, and the third $9.50. He has given you $100 and told you to purchase 100 pens in any combination as long as you spend exactly $100 for 100 pens. Just one solution is possible. Can you find it? Hint: Familiarity with solving simultaneous equations would be helpful here.

## 297

Three of these five figures fit together to create a triangle. Which ones are they?

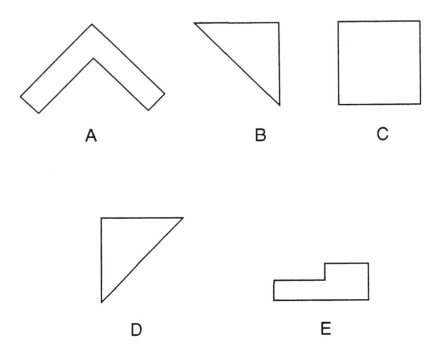

A

B

C

D

E

## 298

Here's a problem that will test your "layered thinking" ability. Give yourself about a minute to solve this puzzle.

Imagine that you have four kings and three queens from an ordinary deck of playing cards. (If you have access to a deck, the puzzle is more fun.)

The object of the game is to arrange the seven cards in an order that will result in an alternating pattern of K, Q, K, Q, K, Q, K. The seven cards must be held facedown. Move every other card, beginning with the first, to the bottom of the deck. Beginning with the second card, place every other card faceup on the table to reach the desired alternating pattern.

Remember, the first card goes to the bottom of the facedown pile, the second card goes faceup on the table, the third card goes to the bottom, the fourth card goes faceup, etc., until all seven are on the table.

What is the beginning arrangement of the cards?

## 299

Mary has placed two chocolate cupcakes in one drawer of her kitchen. In another drawer, she has placed a chocolate and a vanilla cupcake; and in a third drawer, two vanilla cupcakes. Her brother knows the arrangement of the cupcakes, but doesn't know which drawers contain each arrangement.

Mary opens one of the drawers, pulls out a chocolate cupcake, and says to her brother, "If you can tell me what the chances are that the other cupcake in this drawer is chocolate, I'll let you have any cupcake you like."

What are the chances that the other cupcake is chocolate?

## 300

A team of cryptologists is in the process of developing a four-digit code that can never be broken. They know that if the code begins with 0, 5, or 7, it can be cracked. What is the greatest number of four-digit codes the team can use that won't be broken?

## 301

Assuming that P, Q, and R have values other than those already used, what number, excluding 0, is it impossible for R to be?

$$
\begin{array}{r}
2\ P\ 4 \\
Q\ 5 \\
+\ \ R\ 7 \\
\hline
4\ 0\ 7
\end{array}
$$

## 302

If $7^{13}$ is divided by 10, what will the remainder be? You may get the wrong answer if you try to solve this on some calculators.

## 303

If the first three of the following statements are true, is the conclusion true or false?

All Nebraskans are Cornhusker fans.
Some Cornhusker fans are also Hawkeye fans.
Some Hawkeye fans are also Cyclone fans.
Therefore, some Nebraskans are Cyclone fans.

## 304

In a strange, distant land, they have a slightly different number system than ours. For instance, $4 \times 6 = 30$ and $4 \times 7 = 34$. Based on this, what is the value of $5 \times 4 \times 7$ in this land? Hint: Remember this is a number *system*.

## 305

Ann, Boobie, Cathy, and Dave are at their monthly business meeting. Their occupations are author, biologist, chemist, and doctor, but not necessarily in that order. Dave just told the biologist that Cathy was on her way with doughnuts. Ann is sitting across from the doctor and next to the chemist. The doctor was thinking that Boobie was a goofy name for parents to choose, but didn't say anything.

What is each person's occupation?

## 306

See if you can establish a pattern to fill in the fourth grid in this sequence puzzle.

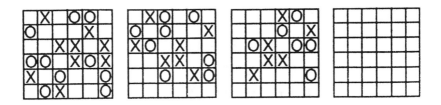

## 307

The sum of the infinite series ½ + ¼ + ⅛ + 1/16 ... equals 1.
What is the sum of the infinite series ¼ + 1/16 + 1/64 + 1/256 ... ?

## 308

This puzzle requires analytical reasoning. Determine the relationships between the figures and words to find two solutions.

○○○ = **LAG**          **RAB** = ○
                               ○

◇ ◇ = **LEB**

◇ ◇ ◇ = **?**          **REG** = ◇
                               ◇
                               ◇

**REBRAG** = **?**

## 309

Here's another opportunity to use analytical reasoning, but this puzzle has a slightly different twist.
In a foreign language:
*"Kaf navcki roi"* means "Take three pieces."
*"Kir roi palt"* means "Hide three coins."
*"Inoti kaf kir"* means "Cautiously take coins."
How would you say "Hide pieces cautiously" in this language?

# 310

Seventy-eight percent of all people are gum chewers, and thirty-five percent of all people are under the age of fifteen. Given that a person has been selected at random, what is the probability that the person is not a gum chewer and above age fifteen?

# 311

What is the next letter in this series?

**A    B    D    O    P    Q    ?**

# 312

**A.**  $2^{65}$
**B.**  $(2^{64} + 2^{63} + 2^{62} \ldots 2^2 + 2^1 + 2^0)$

In comparing the values of A and B, which of these statements is correct?

B is $2^{64}$ larger than A.
A is $2^{64}$ larger than B.
A and B are equal.
B is larger than A by 1.
A is larger than B by 1.

# 313

Classic puzzles are fun to revisit now and then, especially if there's a new twist.

In this puzzle, see if you can be as successful as John in retrieving water for his mother. The new twist? The buckets are different sizes.

John's mother told him to go to the river and bring back exactly 9 gallons of water in one trip. She gave him a six-gallon bucket and a five-gallon bucket to complete his task. Of course, John's mother told him she'd bake his favorite cake if he came back with the 9 gallons.

John had his cake and ate it, too. Can you?

## 314

**1881 : 1961 :: 6009 : ?**

## 315

In the world of physics, sometimes things that appear to move forward are actually moving backward. Knowing this, can you complete this analogy?

**EMIT : STAR :: TIME : ?**

## 316

What is the next number in this series?

**1  9  18  25  27  21  ?**

## 317

Nine men and seven women pick as much corn in five days as seven men and eleven women pick in four days. Who are the better corn pickers and by how much?

## 318

Puzzles 318 to 325 are all composed of numbers, but that doesn't necessarily mean that the numbers contained in any given problem are mathematically related. Your mind will have to be flexible to determine what type of relationship the numbers in the series have with each other. There are no holds barred, and each puzzle may have a solution more obvious than you realize at first.

What is the next number in this series?

**1  2  4  13  31  112  ?**

## 319

What is the next number in this series?

**1   4   2   8   5   7   ?**

Hint: This might be just a fraction of what you think.

## 320

What is the missing number in this series?

**9   3   15   7   12   ?   13   5   17   11**

## 321

What is the next number in this series?

**0   2   4   6   8   12   12   20   16   ?**

## 322

What is the missing number in this series?

**16   21   26   26   12   ?   19**

## 323

What is the next number in this series?

**3   4   11   16   27   36   ?**

## 324

What is the next number in this series?

**224   1   8   30   5   ?**

## 325

No puzzle book would be complete without at least one anagram. Here is a phrase that, when unscrambled, spells the name of a famous person. The phrase gives a small hint relating to the person's identity.

### BEEN IN STAR LITE

## 326

Imagine a 3 × 3 × 3-inch opaque cube divided into twenty-seven 1-inch cubes. Quickly, what are the maximum number of 1-inch cubes that can be seen by one person from any point in space?

## 327

What are the values of §, ⊗, and ¶?

§ + § + § + ⊗ = § + § + ⊗ + ⊗ + ⊗ = ¶ + ¶

$$¶ - § = 6$$

## 328

Below are four grids. See if you can determine the logic used in arriving at each successive grid. What would the next grid look like?

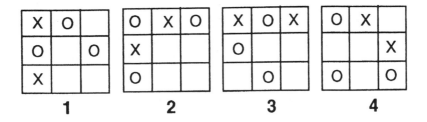

## 329

Bill is standing on the ground, looking directly at one of the faces of a new museum built in the shape of a four-sided pyramid. All the sides are identical.

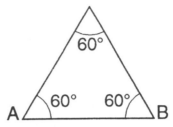

At night, each edge of the pyramid is illuminated with an array of colored lights. Bill's friend Judy is in an airplane touring the area. When her plane, which is several thousand feet high, flies directly over the top of the pyramid, Bill asks her, via walkie-talkie, if she can tell what angle lines A and B make at the peak of the pyramid. Judy answers without hesitation, but it's not what Bill expected. Why?

## 330

Nitram Rendrag, the world's most renowned puzzle creator, often rents a private dining car on the Charlotte–Greensboro–Charlotte turn-around shuttle. The railroad charges Rendrag $120 for the trip. On a recent trip, the conductor informed Rendrag that there were two students at the Franklin station who wished to go from Franklin to Greensboro and back to Franklin. Franklin is halfway between Charlotte and Greensboro. Rendrag asked the conductor to let the students ride with him.

When the students boarded Rendrag's car, he said, "If you can tell me the mathematically correct price you should pay for your portion of the trip, I'll let you ride for free. Remember, your answer has to be mathematically equitable for all of us." How much should the students pay for their journey?

# 331

Of the four choices below, which best completes this figure analogy?

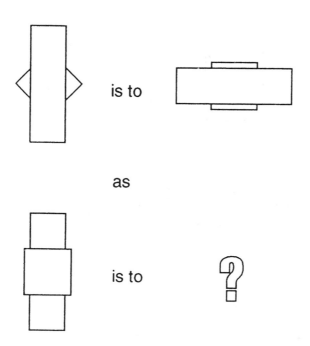

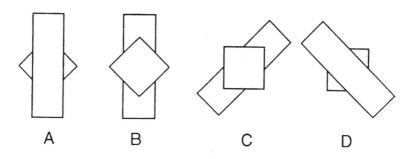

A      B      C      D

# 332

Of the four choices below, which best completes this figure analogy?

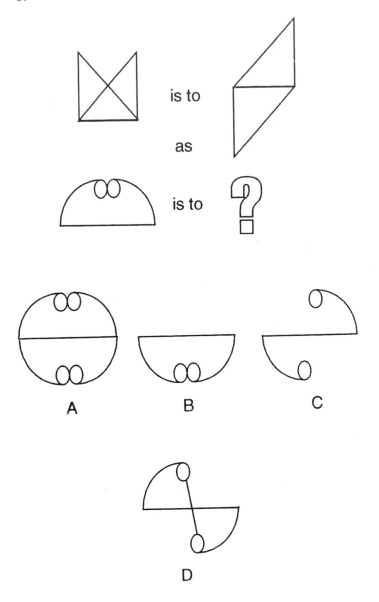

## 333

Which of the five choices completes this analogy?

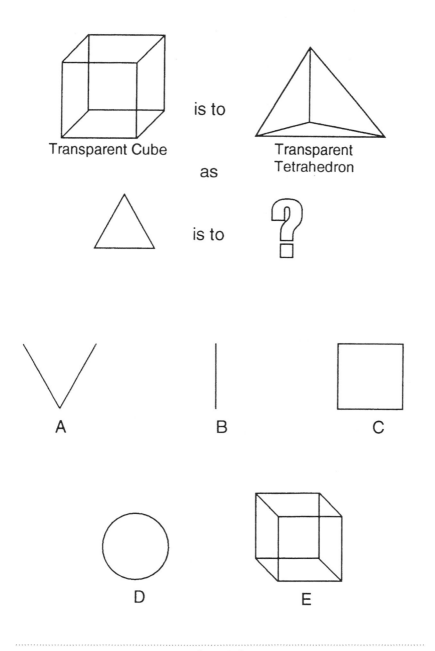

Transparent Cube

is to

as

Transparent Tetrahedron

is to

A

B

C

D

E

Complete this analogy.

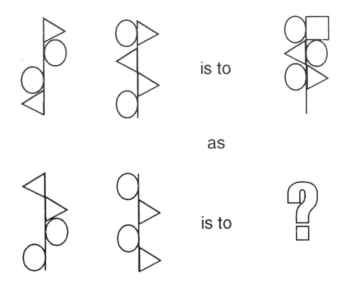

Which one of the following figures does not belong? Hint: Don't consider symmetry.

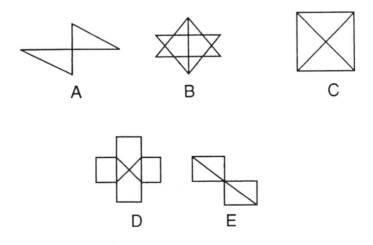

A      B      C

D      E

# 336

A northbound freight train with 100 boxcars will soon meet a southbound freight train with 100 boxcars in single-track territory. They'll meet near a siding track that has a maximum capacity of 80 boxcars. The engines of the southbound train are too heavy to enter any portion of the siding trackage.

With the following information, is it possible for the two trains to get around each other and continue on their trip in the same direction as they started? If so, how?

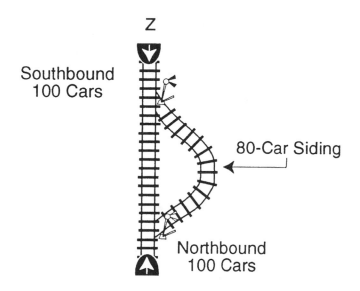

**Basic RR Rules**

No cars may roll freely by themselves.
All cars and engines have couplers on both ends.

The siding track has switches on both ends.
Engines can move in either direction.
Both trains have radio communications and cabooses.

## 337

Find the hidden phrase or title.

## 338

Find the hidden phrase or title.

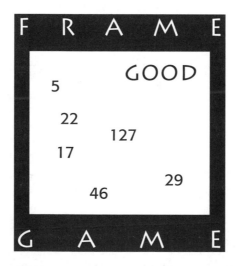

## 339

A previous puzzle asks how many revolutions a rotating coin can make around a duplicate fixed coin in one full rotation. The answer is two. This is a variation of that puzzle, and you may be surprised at the answer.

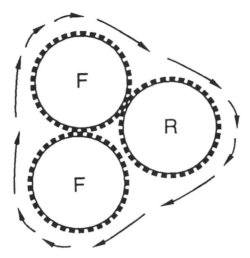

A rotating gear in a diesel engine revolves around two fixed gears and looks like this.

All three gears are identical in size. How many revolutions will Gear R make in one full rotation around the fixed gears?

## 340

Sara rows down the Snake River at a rate of 4 m.p.h. with the current. After she's traveled for two hours, she turns around and rows back against the current to where she started. It takes her four hours to return. What is Sara's rowing rate in still water? What is the rate of the Snake River?

## 341

Candace is Jane's daughter's aunt's husband's daughter's sister. What is the relationship between Candace and Jane?

## 342

English puzzler Henry Dudeney was a master at creating all types of intriguing train puzzles. From the speeds of roaring locomotives to the times on station clocks, his train puzzles demonstrated elegant simplicity while testing the solver's deductive reasoning power.

In keeping with the spirit of Dudeney's train puzzles, Professor Fractal was taking his best math-prize student to Kensington Station to board a train for Leeds, for the British Isles Math Contest. As they entered the depot, the station clock chimed six o'clock. The professor turned to his math whiz and said, "If you can tell me at what time, immediately prior to six o'clock, the hands of the clock were exactly opposite each other, I'll buy you dinner before your departure."

The student enjoyed a delicious London broil. What was the exact time in hours, minutes, and seconds when the hands of the clock were opposite each other, immediately prior to six o'clock?

## 343

See if you can deduce the logic of the letters in and around the circles to determine what the missing letter is inside the last circle.

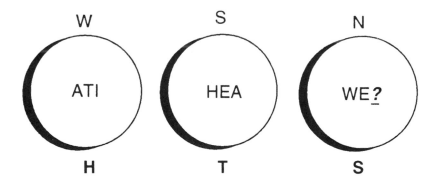

## 344

What's the missing number?

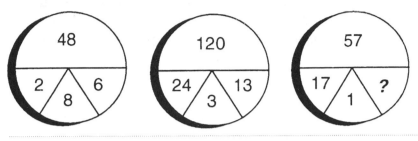

## 345

If one type of weight can balance either 5 gold coins or 4 silver coins, then ten weights of the same type can balance 20 gold coins and how many silver coins in the same scale pan?

## 346

Sometimes in school or business, we are given information that looks impossible to decipher, only to find out that applying a little "elbow grease" aids in sorting things out. Below are several statements that attempt to form some relationships between the letters A, B, C, and D, and the numbers 1, 2, 3, and 4. Using the following information, see if you can straighten out this confusion and identify each letter with its associated number.

If A is 1, then B is not 3.
If B is not 1, then D is 4.
If B is 1, then C is 4.
If C is 3, then D is not 2.
If C is not 2, then D is 2.
If D is 3, then A is not 4.

*Hint*: Make a grid with A, B, C, and D on one side and 1, 2, 3, and 4 on the other. Then make some assumptions.

## 347

Linda wants to drain the water out of a 55-gallon barrel. She has the choice of using either a 2-inch-diameter hose or two 1-inch-diameter hoses to drain the barrel. Which will drain the barrel faster—the 2-inch hose or the two 1-inch hoses? Will they drain the water equally fast?

## 348

It seems that every puzzle writer has a friend who is a brilliant logician and who makes a living solving impossible problems for the government or tracking down criminals.

Molly O'Coley is of that rare breed. The 'Mazin' Ms. Molly, as she's known to Scotland Yard, sent me a note some time ago about a notorious international criminal who was jailed due to her efforts. Much secrecy had surrounded the trial because the prosecution didn't want the public to know the large sum of money recovered by Ms. Molly. They felt that information might hinder future efforts to bring the criminal's associates to trial.

Below is the total contents of Ms. Molly's note to me. Each letter of this note stands for a number, and the total is the sum that Ms. Molly recovered. Can you find the exact amount?

$$
\begin{array}{r}
\text{TRAIL} \\
+\ \text{TRIAL} \\
\hline
\text{GUILTY}
\end{array}
$$

### Y = 3

Note: The letter Y is not part of the addition problem. I later discovered that the Y = 3 also indicated the number of associates the criminal had. Ms. Molly found them in Stuttgart and had them extradited to London.

## 349

In this alphametic, if you find that one of the letters is equal to nine, then another letter must equal 5 and still another must be 4. Let E = 4 and V = 7.

$$
\begin{array}{cc}
\textbf{A} & \textbf{FIVE} \\
+\ \textbf{A} & \textbf{FOUR} \\
\hline
\textbf{IF} & \textbf{NINE} \\
\end{array}
$$

## 350

After trying several times to reach my wife by phone and failing, due to problems with the telephone, I arrived home to find this curious coded message left next to the telephone. Can you decipher my wife's message?

9368   86   289   2   639   74663

## 351

There are 100 students applying for summer jobs in a university's geology/geography department. Ten of the students have never taken a course in geology or geography. Sixty-three of the students have taken at least one geology course. Eighty-one have taken at least one geography course.

What is the probability that of the 100 applicants any student selected at random has taken either geography or geology, but not both?

How many students have taken at least one course in both geology and geography?

## 352

Find the hidden phrase or title.

## 353

Here's another old puzzle with a different twist. Two friends were talking, and the first one said, "Do you remember the brainteaser about a drawer full of black and blue socks?" His friend replied he wasn't sure. "The object is to determine the minimum number of socks you'd have to pick in the dark in order to have a pair of the same color," said the first friend. "Yes," said the second friend, "I remember. The answer is three." "That's right," replied the storyteller. "Quickly now, tell me the minimum number of socks you'd need to take from the drawer if it contained twenty-four blue socks and twenty black socks and you wanted to be assured of a pair of black socks?"

## 354
**(17:8) : (25:7) :: (32:5) : (  ?  :  ?  )**

Find the hidden phrase or title.

At a gathering of mathematicians, everyone shook hands with four other people, except for two people, who shook hands with only one other person (not each other).

If one person shakes hands with another, each person counts as one handshake.

What is the minimum number of people who could have been present? What is the total number of handshakes that took place?

You've just thrown your first two dice in a craps game and your point is 10. This means that you must continue to roll the dice until you roll another 10 to make your point. If you roll a 7 before you roll another 10, you lose.

What are your chances of winning with 10 as your point?

## 358

The numbers 1 through 6 are arranged so that any number resting between and below two other numbers is the difference between those two numbers.

Using numbers 1 through 10, fill in the X's below to create a "difference triangle" with the same conditions. If you'd like a little stiffer challenge, try this using the numbers 1 through 15 in five rows.

## 359

This puzzle is a variation of the game nim, named by Harvard mathematics professor Charles Bouton in 1901. Mathemagician Martin Gardner discusses a version of the game in his book *Entertaining Mathematical Puzzles*.

In Gardner's version, coins are arranged like this:

Two players take turns removing the coins. More than one coin can be removed on a turn as long as they are in the same row. The person who is forced to take the last coin is the loser. Gardner asks the reader if an ironclad winning first move can be determined. The answer is yes. The first player removes three coins from the bottom row.

In our version of nim, an extra coin is added to the top so that the ten coins are arranged like this.

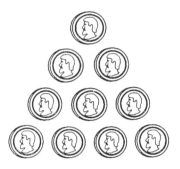

The rules are basically the same, except that in our game, if more than one coin is removed from any row, the coins must be adjacent to each other. For example, if a coin had been removed from the bottom row by a player, the other player may *not* pick up the remaining three coins.

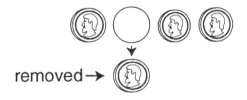

In this case, the second player may pick up the coin on the left or either or both on the right. In our version, there are two winning first moves. What are they?

# 360

Logician George Summers's puzzles are among the best. His logic brainteasers offer a clear, straightforward presentation of the puzzle, yet fully test the deductive reasoning process of even the best puzzle enthusiasts. His book *The Great Book of Mind Teasers & Mind Puzzlers* will keep you busy for days.

In one of his creations, which could be called the "letter cross," letters represent numbers, and you must make several deductions to come up with the value of each letter.

Here is a version of a letter cross puzzle. Although not particularly difficult, it still requires several steps for its solution. Solve this, and you'll be ready to tackle some of Summers's crunchers.

$$A \ B \ C \ D$$
$$E$$
$$F$$
$$G \ H \ I \ J$$

$$A + B + C + D = D + E + F + G = G + H + I + J = 17$$

$A = 4$ and $J = 0$. Using all digits from 0 through 9 only once, find the values for B, C, D, E, F, and G.

There is more than one correct answer. Several numbers are interchangeable.

# 361

Here's a punchy clue to a series question.

Cubes and squares can be one and the same,
But if this so happens, they need a new name.
Squbes sounds OK, so I'll leave it at that,
But can you now tell me where the next one is at?

$$64 \quad 729 \quad 4,096 \quad 15,625 \quad \underline{\quad ? \quad}$$

## 362

There are five boxes such that Box C fits into Box A, Box D fits into Box B or Box C, and Box A is not the largest.

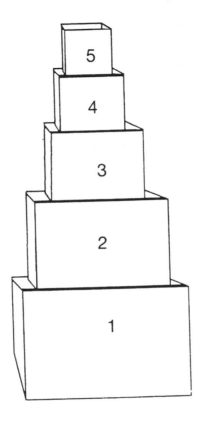

As you can see, Box 1 is the largest and each progressive box is smaller, so that Box 5 is the smallest. The number of the box that represents Box A plus the number of the box that represents Box E is equal to the number of the box that represents Box D plus the number of the box that represents Box C. Determine the size of Boxes A through E from largest to smallest.

# 363

Three identical bags contain colored balls. Each bag has one red and one white ball. A ball is drawn out of Bag 1, another out of Bag 2, and another out of Bag 3.

What are the chances that you'll end up with exactly 2 white balls?

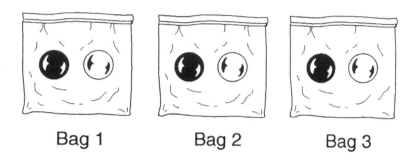

Bag 1          Bag 2          Bag 3

# 364

Three straight cuts on a single plane through a cube will result in a maximum of eight pieces. What is the maximum number of pieces that will result when four planar cuts are made through a cube? The slices may not be rearranged between cuts.

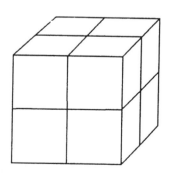

Take three coins and arrange them like this.

1

2   3

Now, if you wanted to turn the triangle upside down using the minimum number of moves, you would move Coin 1 below Coins 2 and 3 like this.

2   3

1

What is the minimum number of coins you need to move to turn the following triangle upside down?

Can you find a general pattern or formula for predicting how many coins you must move to turn any triangle of N length upside down?

# 366

This game, often called the triangle pegboard game, has been around a long time and offers a good challenge. Maybe you've seen it in restaurants throughout the country.

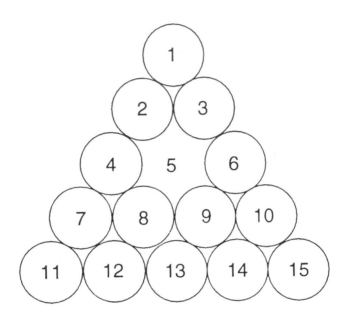

The object of the game, which can also be played with coins, is to jump one peg over another, staying inside the triangle. After jumping over a peg, remove that peg. The goal is to end up with only one peg. Begin with 14 pegs or coins and leave the middle hole open. There is only one solution (two if you count its mirror image). If you've tried this puzzle, you know that it can drive you crazy if you get off on the wrong track.

On the next page are the first six moves towards the correct solution. Of course, if you want to go it alone, stop reading here.

Take fourteen markers or coins and arrange them as shown. Don't forget to remove a marker after you've jumped over it.

Here's your start.

Step 1—Move 12 to 5.
Step 2—Move 10 to 8.
Step 3—Move 14 to 12.
Step 4—Move 3 to 10.
Step 5—Move 2 to 9.
Step 6—Move 7 to 2.

There are thirteen jumps in all. The remaining seven moves are in the Answers section.

# 367

Imagine that you must build a tunnel through eight identical cubes. The tunnel must be continuous and start from any of the three exposed faces of Cube 1. The tunnel has to pass through each of the eight cubes only once, and it cannot cut through any place where more than two cubes meet. How many cubes must be excluded as the tunnel's final or exit cube? What are their numbers?

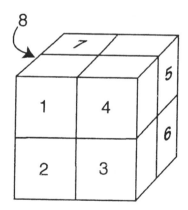

Below are five different sides of a solid object constructed out of several identical cubes fused together. What does the sixth side look like?

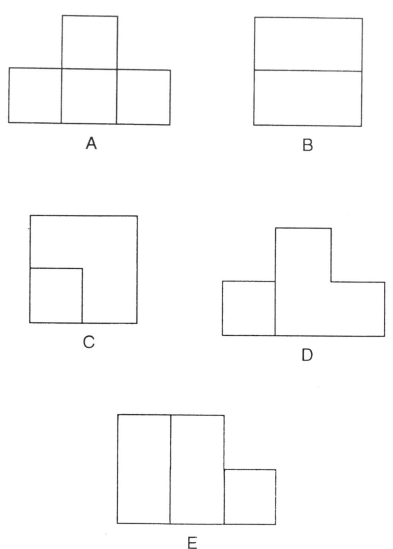

A

B

C

D

E

## 369

Find the hidden phrase or title.

## 370

Arrange twelve toothpicks into a sort of window pane. Rearrange only three of them to create ten different triangles of any size.

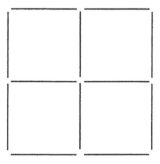

## 371

Find the hidden phrase or title.

## 372

Four friends, Bob, Bill, Pat, and Tom, are nicknamed Rabbit, Walleye, Fly, and Bear—but not necessarily in that order.

   a. Pat can run faster than Rabbit, but can't lift as much weight as Fly.

   b. Rabbit is stronger than Tom, but slower than Walleye.

   c. Bob is faster than both Pat and Bear, but not as strong as Rabbit.

What is the nickname of each friend?

## 373

A certain blend of grass seed is made by mixing Brand A at $9.00 a pound with Brand B at $4.00 a pound. If the blend is worth $7.00 a pound, how many pounds of Brand A are needed to make 40 pounds of the blend?

# 374

Two rockets are launched simultaneously from two different positions.

Rocket A will land at the same spot from which Rocket B was launched, and Rocket B will land at the same spot where Rocket A was launched, allowing a small distance to the left or right to avoid a midair collision.

The rockets are launched from the same angle, and therefore travel the same distance both vertically and horizontally. If the rockets reach their destinations in one and nine hours, respectively, after passing each another, how much faster is one rocket than the other?

A                                                B

# 375

Your chemistry teacher asks you to convert temperatures from one system of measurement to another. These are new systems for determining temperatures, so the classic conversions from Centigrade, Fahrenheit, and Kelvin don't apply.

You are told that 14° in the first system is equal to 36° in the second system. You also know that 133° in the first system is equal to 87° in the second.

What is the method or formula for converting one system to the other?

At what temperature will both thermometers read the same?

## 376

Here is a sequence of five figures. What would the sixth figure look like?

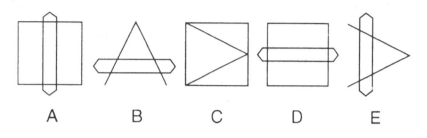

A          B          C          D          E

## 377

One of these figures doesn't belong with the rest. Don't be concerned about symmetry. Which doesn't belong? Why?

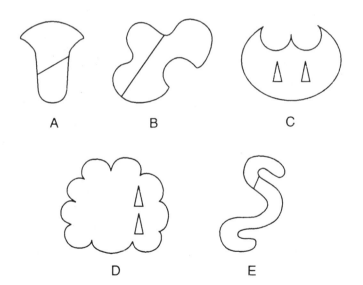

A          B          C

D          E

## 378

Apollona Constantino has 57 of them. Maggie Lieber has 36 of them. Paul Furstenburg has 45 of them. Based on the above, how many of them does Mary Les have?

# 379

How many individual cubes are in this configuration? All rows and columns in the figure are complete unless you actually see them end.

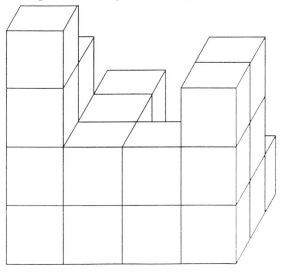

# 380

Thirteen boys and girls wait to take their seats in the same row in a movie theater. The row is thirteen seats long. They decide that after the first person sits down, the next person has to sit next to the first. The third sits next to one of the first two and so on until all thirteen are seated. In other words, no person except the first can take a seat with empty seats on both sides.

How many different ways can this be accomplished, assuming that the first person can choose any of the thirteen seats?

# 381

Three dollar bills were exchanged for a certain number of nickels and the same number of dimes. How many nickels were there? Read this puzzle to a group of friends and see how long it takes to come up with the answer. You may be surprised!

## 382

In the multiplication puzzle below, $x$, $y$, and $z$ represent different digits. What is the sum of $x$, $y$, and $z$?

$$\begin{array}{r} yx \\ \times\ 7 \\ \hline zxx \end{array}$$

## 383

Alex, Ryan, and Steven are sports fans. Each has a different favorite sport among football, baseball, and basketball. Alex does not like basketball; Steven does not like basketball or baseball. Name each person's favorite sport.

## 384

Let's say 26 zips weigh as much as 4 crids and 2 wobs. Also, 8 zips and 2 crids have the same weight as 2 wobs. How many zips have the weight of 1 wob?

## 385

Find the hidden phrase or title.

F R A M E

Look U Leap

G A M E

## 386

There is a certain logic shared by the following four circles. Can you determine the missing number in the last circle?

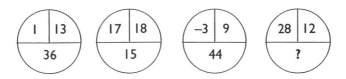

## 387

What is ½ of ⅔ of ⅗ of 240 divided by ½?

## 388

Find the hidden phrase or title.

## 389

The three words below can be rearranged into two words that are also three words! Can you decipher this curious puzzle?

**the red rows**

## 390

Can you determine the next letter in the following series?

**A   C   F   H   K   M   ?**

## 391

One of the figures below lacks a common characteristic that the other five figures have. Which one is it and why?

*Hint:* This does not have to do with right angles or symmetry.

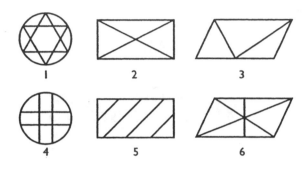

## 392

Find the hidden phrase or title.

## 393

A car travels from point A to point B (a distance of one mile) at 30 miles per hour. How fast would the car have to travel from point B to point C (also a distance of one mile) to average 60 miles per hour for the entire trip?

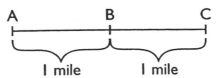

## 394

Try your luck at this "trickle-down" puzzle. Starting at the top, change one letter of each succeeding word to arrive at the word at the bottom.

**T O O K**

———————

———————

———————

**B U R N**

## 395

If the length of a rectangle is increased by 25 percent and its width is decreased by 25 percent, what is the percentage of change in its area?

## 396

A friend has a bag containing two cherry gumdrops and one orange gumdrop. She offers to give you all the gumdrops you want if you can tell her the chances of drawing a cherry gumdrop on the first draw and the orange gumdrop on the second draw. Can you meet your friend's challenge?

## 397

The design on the left is made up of three paper squares of different sizes, one on top of the other. What is the minimum number of squares needed to create the design on the right?

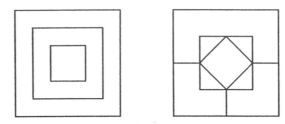

## 398

Here's a variation on an old classic. On what side of the line does the "R" go?

## 399

Find the hidden phrase or title.

## 400

Given the initial letters of the missing words, complete this sentence.

### There are 100 Y in a C.

## 401

If I tripled one-quarter of a fraction and multiplied it by that fraction, I would get one-twelfth. What is the original fraction?

## 402

Two toy rockets are heading directly for each other. One is traveling at 50 miles per hour and the other is traveling at 70 miles per hour. How far apart will these two rockets be one minute before they collide?

## 403

Find the hidden phrase or title.

## 404

Think of five squares that are the same size. In how many ways can these five squares be combined, edge to edge? (No mirror images allowed.)

## 405

What number is four times one-third the number that is one-sixteenth less than three-thirty-seconds?

## 406

Below are five words. By adding the same three letters at the beginning of each word, you can come up with five new words. What three letters will do the trick?

**HER**
**ION**
**OR**
**IF**
**TO**

## 407

If $x^2$ is larger than 9, which of the following is true?

    a.  $x$ is greater than 0.
    b.  0 is greater than $x$.
    c.  $x$ is equal to 0.
    d.  $x^3$ is greater than 0.
    e.  There is insufficient information to determine a solution.

## 408

Based on the following information, how many pleezorns does Ahmad Adziz have?

                Molly O'Brien has 22 pleezorns.
                Debbie Reynolds has 28 pleezorns.
                Roberto Montgomery has 34 pleezorns.

## 409

What is 10 percent of 90 percent of 80 percent?

## 410

Find the hidden phrase or title.

## 411

A mixture of chemicals costs $40 per ton. It is composed of one type of chemical that costs $48 per ton and another type of chemical that costs $36 per ton. In what ratio were these chemicals mixed?

## 412

Find the hidden phrase or title.

## 413

How many triangles of any size are in the figure below?

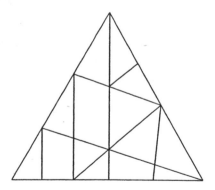

## 414

If the ratio of $5x$ to $4y$ is 7 to 8, what is the ratio of $10x$ to $14y$?

## 415

Decipher the following cryptogram:

**WLA'P XLJAP RLJO XGMXBSAE NSQLOS PGSR GCPXG.**

## 416

Find the hidden phrase or title.

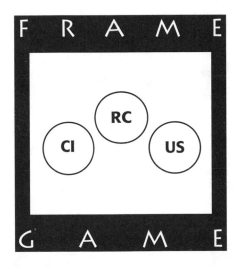

## 417

How many four-letter words can you find in the word "twinkle"? (Try for at least 15.)

## 418

Do this quickly: Write down twelve thousand twelve hundred twenty-two.

## 419

Below are four sets of letters that are related in a way known to virtually everyone. Can you find the missing two letters? (*Hint:* Some people have been known to take months to solve this!)

**ON**
**DJ**
**FM**
**AM**
**? ?**

## 420

Find the hidden phrase or title.

## 421

Find the hidden phrase or title.

## 422

In the strange land of Doubledown the alphabet appears to be hieroglyphics, but it isn't really much different from ours. Below is one of the Doubledown months spelled out. Which month of ours is comparable?

## 423

Which is larger, $3^7 + 7^3$ or the sum of $4^6 + 6^4$? No calculators, please.

## 424

Unscramble this word:

**GORNSIMMAROCI**

## 425

Given the initial letters of the missing words, complete this sentence.

**There is one W on a U.**

## 426

Below are six rays. Choosing two of the rays, how many angles of less than 90 degrees can you form? (Angle ACB is less than 90 degrees.)

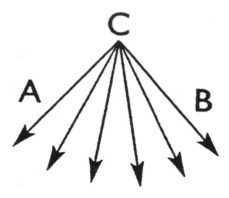

## 427

By arranging all nine integers in a certain order, it is possible to come up with fractions equal to ½, ⅓, ¼, ⅕, ⅙, ⅐, ⅛, and ⅑. See if you can come up with one of these.

$$\text{Example: } \frac{1}{8} = \frac{3,187}{25,496}$$

## 428

Find the hidden phrase or title.

## 429

What are the two missing numbers in the series below?

**8, 15, 10, 13, 12, 11, 14, 9, 16, 7, ?, ?**

## 430

What is the value of **z** in the following problem? (Each number is a positive integer between 0 and 9.)

$$x$$
$$y$$
$$+z$$
$$\overline{xy}$$

## 431

Referring back to the last puzzle, where **z** was found to be 9, what is the value of **x**?

$$x$$
$$y$$
$$\underline{+z}$$
$$xy$$

## 432

Most of us know the following rules of divisibility:
A number is divisible by 2 if it ends in an even digit.
A number is divisible by 3 if the sum of its digits is divisible by 3.
Is there such a rule for dividing by 8?

## 433

Which one of the following five words doesn't belong with the others, and why?

**Pail**
**Skillet**
**Knife**
**Suitcase**
**Doorbell**

## 434

If you wrote down all the numbers from 5 to 83, how many times would you write the number 4?

## 435

Four of the figures below share a characteristic that the fifth figure doesn't have. Can you determine which figure doesn't go with the others and why?

A      B      C      D      E

## 436

Find the hidden phrase or title.

## 437

A certain barrel of candy can be equally divided (without cutting pieces) between five, seven, or thirteen people. What is the least number of pieces of candy the barrel could contain?

## 438

Find the hidden phrase or title.

## 439

Which is greater, 107 percent of 300 or 50 percent of 600?

## 440

What is the value of the following?

$$\frac{1}{3 + \dfrac{1}{3\,^1/_3}}$$

## 441

The diagram below is the beginning of a "magic square" in which all rows and columns and both diagonals add up to 34. Can you fill in the rest of the numbers?

| 1 | 8 | 13 | 12 |
|---|---|----|----|
| 14 |   |    |    |
| 4 |   | 16 |    |
| 15 |   |    |    |

## 442

The diagram below can be drawn without lifting your pencil or crossing any other line. Can you do it?

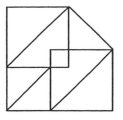

## 443

Imagine that a coin called a "kookla" is equal in value to either 7 gold pieces or 13 silver pieces. If you have 40 kooklas that you want to exchange for both silver and gold pieces and your bank has only 161 gold pieces on hand, how many silver pieces should you expect to receive with the 161 gold pieces?

## 444

The two numbers in each box have the same relationship to each other as do the two numbers in every other box. What is the missing number?

| 3, 8 | −5, 24 | 0, −1 | 9, 80 | 6, ? |

## 445

There are six chairs, each of a different color. In how many different ways can these six chairs be arranged in a straight line?

## 446

Find the hidden phrase or title.

## 447

Do the numbers 9 and 10 go above or below the line?

| 1 | 2 | | | | 6 | | |
|---|---|---|---|---|---|---|---|
| | | 3 | 4 | 5 | | 7 | 8 |

## 448

Find the hidden phrase or title.

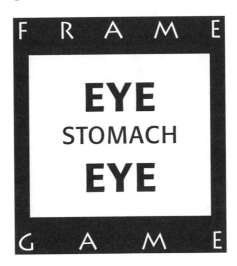

## 449

A concept that math students often find difficult to understand is that a negative multiplied by a negative results in a positive (example: −5 × −5 = 25). Can you come up with a real-life example, in words, to illustrate this?

## 450

Unscramble the following word:

**RGAALEB**

## 451

Without using + or − signs, arrange five 8s so that they equal 9.

## 452

How many individual cubes are in the configuration below? (All rows and columns run to completion unless you see them end.)

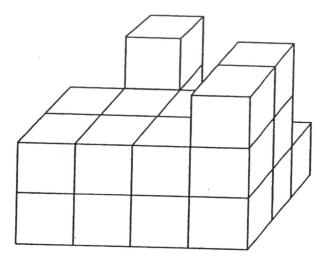

## 453

How many different words can you make from the word "Thanksgiving"? You might be surprised to find how many new words can be made from a word that doesn't contain the letter "e."

## 454

What is $1/10$ divided by $1/2$ divided by $1/5$ times $7/9$?

## 455

Find the hidden phrase or title.

## 456

When the proper weights are assigned, this mobile is perfectly balanced. Can you determine the three missing weights?

(*Hint:* Try starting with the 8-foot section of the mobile. Remember that Distance × Weight = Distance × Weight.)

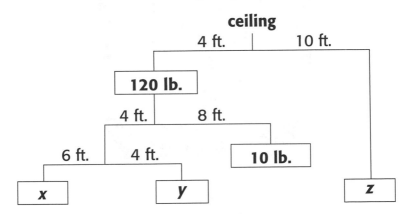

## 457

Below are two numbers represented by *x* and *y*. Regardless of the values of *x* and *y*, all possible answers resulting from the difference in these two numbers share one unique characteristic. What is it?

$$\begin{array}{r} xy \\ - \; yx \\ \hline ?? \end{array}$$

## 458

The perimeter of a square has a value that is two-thirds of the number representing its square footage. What is the size of the square?

## 459

Find the hidden phrase or title.

## 460

In the game of craps, what are the chances that you will be a winner on your first roll by getting either a 7 or an 11?

# 461

Find the hidden phrase or title.

FRAME

Calm       Storm

GAME

# 462

Here's another four-letter "trickle-down" puzzle. Find the three missing words, each with only one letter changed from the previous word, to arrive at **BARN**.

M O O D

_____

_____

_____

B A R N

## 463

What is the value of T in the following puzzle?

$$A + B = H$$
$$H + P = T$$
$$T + A = F$$
$$B + P + F = 30$$
$$A = 2$$

## 464

If five potatoes and six onions cost $1.22 and six potatoes and five onions cost $1.31, what does an onion cost?

## 465

Find the hidden phrase or title.

## 466

Below are 10 matchsticks of equal length. By moving 2 and only 2 matchsticks, can you create 2 squares only, with no leftover matchsticks?

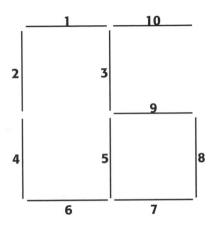

## 467

A bag contains 7 green balls and 3 red ones. What is the probability of randomly taking out 3 green balls in succession without looking if:

*A:* Each ball is replaced before the next draw?
*B:* The balls are not replaced?

## 468

Find the missing number in the following series:

$$\frac{20}{48} \quad \frac{1}{3} \quad \frac{1}{4} \quad \frac{1}{6} \quad \frac{1}{12} \quad ?$$

## 469

Find the hidden phrase or title.

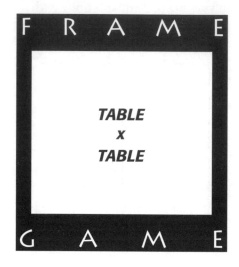

## 470

Given the initial letters of the missing words, complete this sentence.

### There are 206 B in the H B.

## 471

What is the first number having factors that add up to more than the number itself? (Don't include the number itself as one of the factors.)

## 472

What number is ¼ of ⅓ of ⅙ of 432, divided by ⅓?

## 473

Find the hidden phrase or title.

## 474

One hundred people are applying for a sales position that would require them to sell both golf equipment and athletic shoes. Thirteen of the applicants have no prior experience in sales. Sixty-five of the applicants have previously sold golf equipment, and 78 of the applicants have sold athletic shoes. How many of the applicants have experience in selling both golf equipment and athletic shoes?

## 475

What's the difference between 11 yards square and 11 square yards?

## 476

Find the four-letter word that will make new words when added in front of these:

**GUARD**
**LONG**
**TIME**

# 477

Find the hidden phrase or title.

# 478

What is the first year after the year 2000 in which the numbers of the year will read the same right-side-up and upside-down? What is the second year in which this will occur? (No fair using digital numerals, like 2!)

# 479

H is to one as C is to six as N is to ?

## 480

Find the hidden phrase or title.

## 481

A "perfect" number is a number whose factors add up to the number (not including the number itself). For example:

The factors of 6 are 3, 2, and 1 and 3 + 2 + 1 = 6.

The factors of 28 are 14, 7, 4, 2, and 1 and 14 + 7 + 4 + 2 + 1 = 28.

What are the next two perfect numbers?

## 482

What are the chances of flipping a penny four times and getting at least two tails?

Find the hidden phrase or title.

Decipher the following cryptogram. Each letter represents another letter in the alphabet.

**OTD X GACOT ST BPWF WASFTOOX.**

What is the next number in the following series?

**1, 2, 6, 30, 60, 180, 900, 1,800, 5,400, ——**

## 486

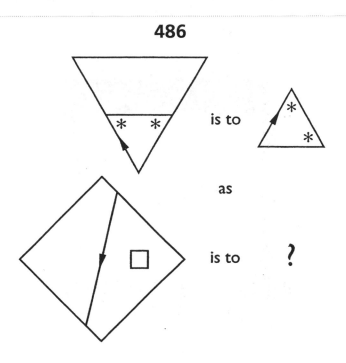

is to

as

is to

?

## 487

A pipe can fill a swimming pool in three hours. A second pipe can fill the pool in two hours. If both pipes are turned on at the same time, how long will it take them to fill the pool?

## 488

I am ten years older than my sister. There was a time when I was three times older than she was, and in one year I will be twice as old as she is. What is my age now?

## 489

Here's an interesting twist on an old series puzzle. See if you can come up with the missing letter. (*Hint:* This problem is best approached with an even hand.)

**T  F  S  E  T  T  F  ?**

## 490

Find the hidden phrase or title.

## 491

Susie's and Sally's last names are Billingsley and Jenkins, but not necessarily in that order. Two of the following statements are false. What is the real name of each person?

**Susie's last name is Billingsley.**
**Susie's last name is Jenkins.**
**Sally's last name is Jenkins.**

## 492

Can you come up with a quick way to find the square of 95 mentally . . . or for that matter the square of 45, 55, 65, etc.?

*Hint.* Think of square numbers above and below each of these numbers.

There is more than one way to do this.

## 493

If you find the correct starting point in the wheel below and move either clockwise or counterclockwise, the letters will spell out a common everyday word. What is the missing letter, and what is the word?

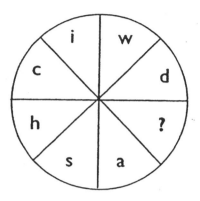

## 494

Find the hidden phrase or title.

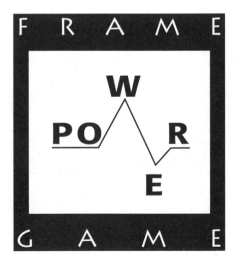

## 495

How many digits must be changed in the following addition problem to make the sum equal 245?

$$
\begin{array}{r}
89 \\
16 \\
+ 98 \\
\hline
\end{array}
$$

## 496

In a certain box of candy, the number of caramels is 25 percent of the number of other candies in the box. What percentage of the entire box are the caramels?

## 497

Find the hidden phrase or title.

## 498

Given the initial letters of the missing words, complete the following sentence. (Hint: Think of hydrogen.)

**There are 106 E in the P T.**

## 499

Change one and only one letter in each successive word to come up with the next word:

**R  O  A  D**

_____

_____

_____

**L  O  O  P**

## 500

One of the following diagrams doesn't fit with the others. Which one is it? Why? Hint: Think symmetry.

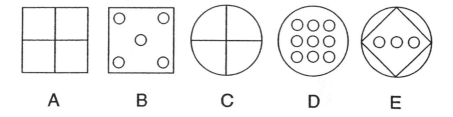

A          B          C          D          E

# 501

Here's fun with roman numerals. See if you can match column A to column B.

| | |
|---|---|
| $\overline{V}$ | 100 |
| $\overline{M}$ | 500 |
| $\overline{C}$ | 1,000 |
| C | 5,000 |
| $\overline{L}$ | 10,000 |
| $\overline{X}$ | 50,000 |
| $\overline{D}$ | 100,000 |
| D | 500,000 |
| M | 1,000,000 |

# 502

Find the hidden phrase or title.

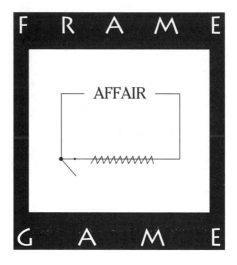

## 503

Using only the letters of the top row on a typewriter, how many 10-letter words can you create?

Remember, the letters are

### QWERTYUIOP

## 504

Find the hidden phrase or title.

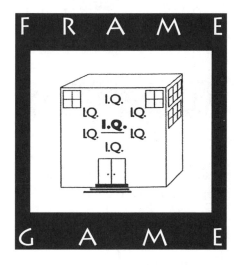

## 505

In a certain game, a ball can fall through any of 50 holes evenly spaced around a wheel. The chance that a ball would fall into any one particular hole is 1 in 50. What are the chances that 2 balls circling the wheel at the same time would fall into the same hole?

## 506

What is the missing number in the following series?

### 84   12   2   ²/₅   ¹/₁₀   ?

## 507

Find the hidden phrase or title.

## 508

A man spent three-fourths of his money and then lost three-fourths of the remainder. He has $6 left. How much money did he start with?

## 509

Molly and Maggie are Martha's mother's son's wife's daughters. What relation is Martha to Molly and Maggie?

## 510

In a foreign language, "rota mena lapy" means large apple tree, "rota firg" means small apple, and "mena mola" means large pineapple. Which word means tree?

## 511

Unscramble the following word:

**O M A H G O L R**

## 512

See if you can determine a relationship among the following circles to find the missing number in the last circle.

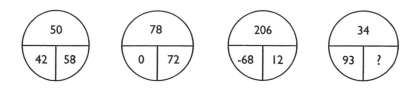

## 513

What is the missing number in the following series?

(*Hint:* Could the numbers represent something other than quantities?)

**13 9 14 4 — 2 5 14 4 9 14 ?**

## 514

Find the hidden phrase or title.

# 515

What familiar four-letter word can be placed in front of each of the following to form four new words?

**Shelf**
**Worm**
**Mobile**
**Mark**

# 516

Given the initial letters of the missing words, complete this sentence:

**There are 180 D in a T.**

# 517

In a shuffled deck of 52 playing cards, you alone are picking the cards out of the deck, and the cards are face down. What are the odds of your drawing the Ace, King, Queen, and Jack of spades in succession:

**1 chance in 208?**
**1 chance in 2,704?**
**1 chance in 6,497,400?**
**1 chance in 1,000,000,000?**

# 518

What number is 4 times $\frac{1}{10}$ the number that is $\frac{1}{10}$ less than $\frac{3}{13}$?

# 519

There's an old puzzle that you have probably seen many times where you are asked to assign the same digit for each letter in the following.

$$\begin{array}{r} \text{SEND} \\ + \text{MORE} \\ \hline \text{MONEY} \end{array}$$

Now try this variation. Let M = 6 and N = 3.

$$\begin{array}{r} \text{SPEND} \\ - \text{MORE} \\ \hline \text{MONEY} \end{array}$$

# 520

How many different squares (of any size) are in this figure?

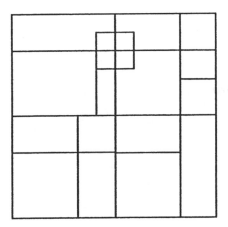

## 521

Find the hidden phrase or title.

## 522

Decipher the following cryptogram:

**SALTS LA ELLG**

## 523

Use three moves to get from the first word to the last.

**B I K E**

———————

———————

———————

**M A T H**

## 524

The blank at the bottom of the second column below could be filled in by any one of three words. What are these words?

| | |
|---|---|
| EVIL | POST |
| LIVE | STOP |
| VILE | TOPS |
| VEIL | _____ |

## 525

Here's a series problem that may require a little extra patience...

**3 11 20 27 29 23 ?**

## 526

Unscramble this word:

**A T T R E S P N A R N**

## 527

Find the hidden phrase or title.

## 528

A squash tournament has six rounds of single elimination for its singles competition. This includes the championship match, and there are no byes. How many players are entered when play begins?

## 529

Given the initial letters of the missing words, complete the following sentence. (*Hint:* Think of Zorba.)

### There are 24 L in the G A.

## 530

What is the smallest number of square sheets of paper of any size that can be placed over each other to form the pattern below?

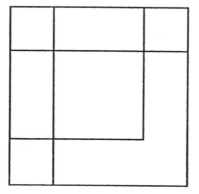

## 531

If you built a four-sided pyramid—not counting the bottom as a side—using ping-pong balls, how many balls would be in a pyramid that had seven layers?

Find the hidden phrase or title.

Shown below is the bottom of a pyramid of black circles and white circles. The colors of the circles in each successive row are determined by the colors of the circles in the row below it. Complete the top three rows.

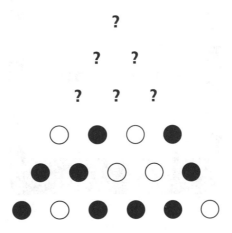

## 534

When the proper weights are assigned, the mobile shown here is in perfect balance. What are the four missing weights?

Hint: distance × weight = distance × weight.

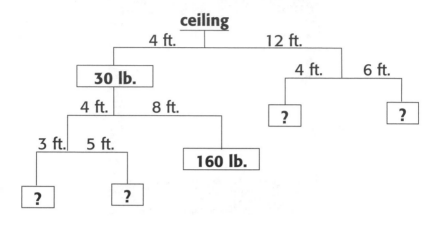

## 535

Find the hidden phrase or title.

## 536

Four friends are going to a concert. When they arrive, there are only five seats together left in the theater. The manager will let all four friends in for free if one of them can tell her how many different seating arrangements are possible for four people with five empty seats. All four are let in free. Could you have given the correct answer?

## 537

What word can be added to the end of each of the following words to form new words?

**MOON**
**SHOE**
**MONKEY**

## 538

In a class of fewer than 30 students, two received a B on a math test, $1/7$ of the class received a C, $\frac{1}{2}$ received a D, and $\frac{1}{4}$ of the class failed the exam. How many students received an A?

## 539

Molly can build a fence in two days. Alex can build the same fence in three days. Their younger brother, Steve, can build the fence in six days. If all three worked together, how long would it take to build the fence?

## 540

Find the hidden phrase or title.

FRAME

corres**4**pondent

GAME

## 541

How many cubes of any size are in the configuration below? (*Hint:* Think of smaller, easier examples. There is an easily recognizable pattern to this puzzle.)

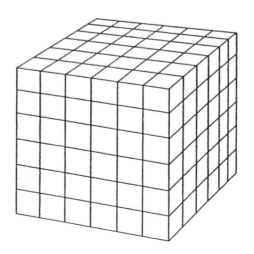

## 542

Arrange the numbers in the boxes so that no two consecutive numbers are next to each other (horizontally, vertically, or diagonally).

|   |   |   |
|---|---|---|
| 1 | 2 |   |
| 3 | 4 | 5 |
| 6 | 7 | 8 |
|   | 9 | 10 |

## 543

If *p* is three-quarters of *q*, *q* is two-thirds of *r*, and *r* is one-half of *s*, what is the ratio of *s* to *p*?

## 544

Find the hidden phrase or title.

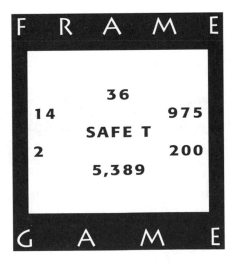

## 545

Four baseball players from the same team—Reggie, Chris, Lou, and Leo—play right field, first base, left field, and catcher, but none of the players and positions correspond in this order. From the following additional information, determine each player's position:

    a) Reggie hits more homers than the catcher but fewer than the left fielder.

    b) Leo and the left fielder are cousins.

## 546

Find the hidden phrase or title.

## 547

An eagle, an elephant, and a walleye have two each. A tiger, a moose, a bear, a turtle, and a snake have one each. Neither a human nor a gorilla has any. What are we talking about?

## 548

Here is a "trickle-down" puzzle. Simply replace one letter per line to arrive at the answer. If you can do it in fewer than the number of moves shown here, so much the better!

**B A N D**

---

---

---

**P I P S**

## 549

A bicycle is three times as old as its tires were when the bicycle was as old as the tires are now. What is the ratio of the tires' current age to the bicycle's current age?

## 550

Quick now, which is bigger, $2^{13}$ or $2^{12} + 2^2$?

## 551

Given the initial letters of the missing words, complete this phrase:

**4 S and 7 Y A**

Find the hidden phrase or title.

Here's an alphametic for you:

**THREE**
**THREE**
**THREE**
**+ ELEVEN**
**TWENTY**

Each letter represents a digit and the value for that letter remains the same throughout. No beginning letter of a word can be zero. Good luck!

## 554

The analogy puzzle below has a different twist. It is a spatial/visual analogy, and the answer is given! How are the Xs in the second grid of each analogy determined?

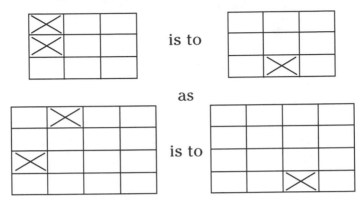

is to ... as ... is to

## 555

Find the hidden phrase or title.

## 556

The starting lineup of a baseball team wants a photograph taken with all nine of the players sitting in a row on a bench. One of the ball players wonders how many different arrangements can be made of the order in which they sit. Do you know?

## 557

Below, on the left, is a list of words, some of which may be unfamiliar. On the right is a list of related, familiar words. Match the words in the second list to those in the first. Take each word on the left and look for the related words you know for sure. Then think of words that are similar to the ones you don't know—for instance, "potent" is like "potentate"—and then look for a reasonable match!

| | |
|---|---|
| 1. gambol | a. turtle |
| 2. fortissimo | b. hats |
| 3. sortie | c. loud |
| 4. millinery | d. power |
| 5. culinary | e. ambiguous |
| 6. ornithology | f. smell |
| 7. odoriferous | g. refined |
| 8. gustatory | h. opposites |
| 9. humus | i. cooking |
| 10. terrapin | j. cow |
| 11. bovine | k. frolic |
| 12. antipodes | l. raid |
| 13. equivocal | m. soil |
| 14. potentate | n. birds |
| 15. urbane | o. taste |

## 558

A ladder was standing perfectly upright against a wall. Suddenly the foot of the ladder slid away from the wall and came to a stop 15 feet from the wall. The top of the ladder had moved only one-fifth of the ladder's length before it came to rest firmly on a windowsill. Do you have enough information to calculate the length of the ladder? If so, what is it?

## 559

There are 10 krits in a flig, 6 fligs in a crat, 5 crats in a wirp, and 7 wirps in a nood. What is the number of krits in a nood divided by the number of fligs in a wirp?

## 560

Find the hidden phrase or title.

## 561

Find the hidden phrase or title.

## 562

What is 2,444 in Roman Numerals?

## 563

Find the next two numbers in this series.

**2 81 6 27 18 9 54 3 ? ?**

## 564

Using any numeral four times and any mathematical symbols you choose, can you produce an equation that will yield the number 300?

## 565

Suppose all counting numbers were arranged in columns as shown below. Under what letter would the number 100 appear?

| A | B | C | D | E | F | G |
|---|---|---|---|---|---|---|
| 1 | 2 | 3 | 4 | 5 | 6 | 7 |
| 8 | 9 | 10 | 11 | 12 | 13 | 14 |
| 15 | 16 | 17 | — | — | — | — |

## 566

Nancy and Audrey set out to cover a certain distance by foot. Nancy walks half the distance and runs half the distance, but Audrey walks half the time and runs half the time. Nancy and Audrey walk and run at the same rate. Who will reach the destination first (or will it be a tie)?

## 567

The following seven numbers share a unique property. What is it?

**1961 6889 6119 8008 8118 6699 6009**

## 568

Find the hidden phrase or title.

## 569

In the puzzle below, the numbers in the second row are determined by the relationships of the numbers in the first row. Likewise, the numbers in the third row are determined by the relationships of the numbers in the second row. Can you determine the relationships and find the missing number?

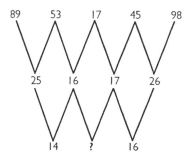

## 570

A mathematician's will stated that his wife should get one-third of his estate, his son one-fifth, his older daughter one-sixth, and his younger daughter $9,000. Who received more, his older daughter or his younger daughter?

## 571

What single-digit number should go in the box with the question mark?

| 6 | 5 | 9 | 2 | 7 |
|---|---|---|---|---|
| 1 | 4 | 3 | 5 | ? |
| 8 | 0 | 2 | 8 | 1 |

## 572

There are 4 clocks in a room. One gains a minute every hour. Another loses a minute every hour. One runs backward at normal speed. The fourth always keeps the correct time. At 7:03 today, they all showed the same time, which was correct. When will this happen again?

## 573

Find the hidden phrase or title.

## 574

While reading a newspaper you notice that four pages of one section are missing. One of the missing pages is page 5. The back page of this section is page 24. What are the other three missing pages?

## 575

Suppose $a$, $b$, and $c$ represent three positive whole numbers. If $a + b = 13$, $b + c = 22$, and $a + c = 19$, what is the value of $c$?

## 576

|   |   |   |
|---|---|---|
| X |   |   |
|   | X | X |
| X |   | X |

is to

|   |   |   |
|---|---|---|
| X |   | X |
|   | X |   |
| X | X |   |

as

|   |   |   |
|---|---|---|
|   |   | X |
| X |   |   |
|   | X |   |

is to

## 577

Below is a "trickle-down" word game. Change one letter and one letter only on each line to arrive at the word on the last line:

**M  O  V  E**

———————

———————

———————

**B  A  R  K**

## 578

Sarah is older than Julie and Maggie. Maggie is older than Paula. Ann is younger than Julie, but older than Paula. Ann is younger than Maggie. Sarah is younger than Liz. Who is the second-oldest woman in this group?

## 579

What is the missing number in the following series?

**13  7  18  10  5  ?  9  1  12  6**

# ANSWERS

**1.** Only once, because the second time you will be subtracting from 24 instead of 30.

**2.** The number 8. (It is made up of two zeroes, one on top of the other.)

**3.** By using Roman numerals. The upper half of XII is VII.

**4.** 1 and 9.

**5.** Any number and 1.

**6.** 2 and 2.

**7.** It is easy to eliminate possibilities. For example, it has to be an even number; none of the digits can be zero (or else the product would be zero); and the product of the digits must be less than or equal to 48 (otherwise two times the product would have three digits). If you think of the remaining possibilities, you will find the answer, $36 = 2 \times 3 \times 6$.

**8.** 1, 2, and 3, because $1 \times 2 \times 3 = 1 + 2 + 3 = 6$.

**9.** $25 = 5^2$ and $36 = 6^2$.

**10.** $99^9 = 9^{387420489}$, which is a number with more than 369 million digits.

**11.** The father is 41 and the son is 14.

**12.** 10 cents.

**13.** $1.10 for the outlet and $0.10 for the light bulb.

**14.** $3 \times 75 = 225$ qualities distributed among 100 persons, so at least 25% of them have all three.

**15.** The number of passing grades is a whole number less than 32, and 5% of it is also a whole number. It can only be 20. If 20 is the number of passing grades, the number of students from New York that took the test is one.

**16.** If half of the 83% tip the usher 10 cents and the other half doesn't, it is the same as if all 83% had tipped him 5 cents, which is the same amount as what the remaining 17% tipped. The usher received 4,800 cents, or more simply, 48 dollars.

**17.** Turn the page upside-down. It will read $108 = 6 \times 18$.

**18.** He will need twenty "9's," one for the numbers 9, 19, 29, 39, 49, 59, 69, 79, 89, 90, 91, 92, 93, 94, 95, 96, 97, and 98, and two for 99.

**19.** At each stop, passengers can buy a ticket for any of the 24 remaining stops. Therefore, the number of tickets will be $25 \times 24 = 600$.

**20.** Let's imagine that the inhabitants are as different as possible (one will be bald, another will have only one hair, another two, another three, and so on, until we get to someone having 100,000 hairs). Inhabitant number 100,002 will have the same number of hairs as someone among the first 100,001 inhabitants. The total population is more than 200,000 people, which means that there will be more than 100,000 inhabitants with the same number of hairs as other people in town.

**21.** Three: one red, one blue, and one brown.

**22.** There are 6 chestnut trees per side, making a total of 12.

**23.** Two birds and one olive tree.

**24.** There is only one winner, so the remaining 110 players were defeated in 110 matches. Therefore, they used 110 balls.

**25.** Twelve muffins. When John ate half the remaining muffins plus three more to leave none, he must have eaten six muffins. So Peter ate half the muffins and left six, meaning that there were twelve to start.

**26.** The shepherd that is talking had 5 sheep and the other one had 7.

**27.** Three cages and four canaries.

**28.** Each sardine costs 1 dollar. Therefore, 7½ sardines would cost 7½ dollars.

**29.** Since ½ brick weighs 3 pounds, 1½ bricks weigh 9 pounds.

**30.** Since 18 sardines is the same as 1½ dozen, they cost 9½ dollars.

**31.** Since 1 man eats 1 pie in 1½ minutes, 1 man eats 20 pies in 30 minutes, which means 3 men eat 60 pies in 30 minutes.

**32.** 11 times (one fewer than the number of times he went in).

**33.** Three ducks.

**34.** The person who won three games must have also lost six games, since his opponent won $3. In total, they played 9 games.

**35.** We measure the inside diameter and the height of the liquid, obtaining the volume of the liquid. Then, we turn the bottle upside-down and measure the volume of the empty part. If we add both, we obtain the total capacity of the bottle and can calculate the percentage of the liquid. An easier way is to measure only both heights, because both have the same size base.

**36.** $0.0125

**37.** By leaving a task half done (for example, peeling potatoes) so that the next soldier can finish it, they can do all the tasks in 1 hour and 30 minutes.

**38.** 29 days. One spider would have covered half of the space on the 29th day, and on the 30th day would repeat what had been done, covering the space completely. Two spiders would each have covered half of the space in 29 days, therefore covering the entire area.

**39.** At 8 p.m. Each hour the volume triples, so it is one-third full one hour before it is full.

**40.** If the length of the rope + 2 yards = 3 times the length of the rope, then the rope is 1 yard long.

**41.** If the length is 6 yards + half the length, then half the length is 6 yards. Therefore, it is 12 yards long.

**42.** No mud at all, because a hole can only contain air.

**43.** There are only three people, a daughter, her mother, and her grandmother. The mother received 25 books from the grandmother and then gave 8 to her daughter.

**44.** Dolores is taller than Emily, who is taller than Ann.

**45.** Joan is 6 years older than Rose.

**46.** Emily speaks in a softer voice than Dolores (Emily < Ann < Dolores).

**47.** Peter is sitting between Philip (on his right) and James (on his left).

**48.** A pound of $10 gold coins has twice the amount of gold than half a pound of $20 coins. Therefore, it is worth more.

**49.** The store lost $40 given as change plus the value of the umbrella, $10. The transaction was only between the sales person and the customer. The bank teller did not take part in the transaction.

**50.** The pitcher with water contains exactly the same amount of wine as water in the pitcher of wine. Both pitchers have the same volume of liquid before and after mixing water and wine, so mixing them makes no difference.

**51.** He made each candidate ride another candidate's horse. Each one would, of course, try to come in first, because in that way the owner of the horse that a particular candidate was riding would lose the race.

**52.** The weight of the fish bowl increases by the same amount as the weight of the liquid displaced by the fish.

**53.** If it is a traditional scale with two dishes, you can place the apples in one dish and dirt in the other until they balance. Then, replace the apples with weights and you will know the weight of the apples. If it is a spring scale, you weigh the apples first, then write down the mark on the scale and replace the apples with weights until you reach the previous mark. The weights will show the real weight of the apples.

**54.** The reaction of the air that the little bird is pushing down in order to fly will partially affect both the dish of the scale and the floor of the room. The scale will show one pound minus some portion of the 5 ounces that the bird weighs.

If the cage were sealed, the air would affect only the dish of the scale and the scale would continue to read one pound.

**55.** One weighing. Take one ball from the first sack, two from the second, three from the third, and so on until you reach the last sack, from which you take ten balls. Since $1 + 2 + 3 + ... + 9 + 10 = 55$, if all of the balls weighed 10 ounces each, the total weight would be 550 ounces. In this case, the weight will be $550 - N$, where N is the number of the sack containing nine-ounce balls.

**56.** We identify each sack by the number of balls taken from it. We must find a way to obtain different results from all possible sums of the digits that identify the sacks. The easiest way would be powers of 2: 1, 2, 4, 8, 16, ... ($2^0$, $2^1$, $2^2$, $2^3$, $2^4$, ...). Therefore, we will take one ball from one sack, two from another, four from another, etc.

The resulting weight will be $1023 - N$, where N can only be obtained by adding certain sack numbers. If N is 27 ounces, the sacks containing 9-ounce balls will be those from which we took 1, 2, 8, and 16 balls, because, using just the powers of 2, 27 can only be obtained by adding $1 + 2 + 8 + 16$.

Let's call "1" the sack from which we took 1 ball, "2" the one from which we took 2 balls, "3" the one from which we took 4 balls, etc. The number 27, in binary, is 11011. The position of the 1's in this binary sequence reveals the solution. The 1's are in first, second, fourth, and fifth position, which means that the sacks containing the 9-ounce balls are 1, 2, 4, and 5.

**57.** The best solution is to open four links from one of the pieces and use them to join the remaining five parts in one chain. The total cost will be $4 \times 60 = 240$ cents, or $2.40.

**58.** By cutting the third link, we obtain three pieces of one, two, and four links each. The first day, she pays with the one-link part. The second day, she pays with the two-link part and gets the one-link piece back as change. The third day, she pays with the loose link. The fourth day, she pays with the four-link part and receives back the three links, and so on.

**59.** The minimum number of parts that could have been left is 3 (the link that is cut and the two disconnected parts of the chain). The maximum number will be 6, as shown in the figure below.

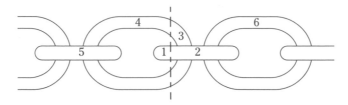

**60.** Two glasses. Pick up the second glass, pour its contents into the ninth glass, and put it back. Then pick up the fourth glass, pour its contents into the seventh glass, and put it back. Note that the seventh and ninth glasses are not moved.

**61.** 100% probability, because if four marbles are in their corresponding cups, the fifth one must be in its corresponding cup, too.

**62.** Three. The first two can be of different colors, white and black, but the third sock will be one of these two colors, and thus complete one pair.

**63.** Four. There are three different colors, so the first three socks may not match, but the fourth one will match one of the previous three socks.

**64.** 13. The first 12 gloves can be six white left gloves and six black left gloves. Therefore, the 13th glove will make a pair with one of the previous 12 gloves. No matter what the first 12 gloves are, if no two have made a pair yet, the 13th will.

**65.** 6. The worst case is to take two white, two black, and the red marble. The sixth marble has to be either white or black.

**66.** Put five marbles in one cup, four in another, and one in another. Put the cup with one marble inside the one containing four. There are other solutions, all based on the same trick. Another solution, for example, involves putting three marbles in one cup, three marbles in the second cup, and four marbles in the third cup, and then putting the second cup inside the third one. This leaves three marbles in the first cup, three marbles in the second cup, and seven marbles in the third cup.

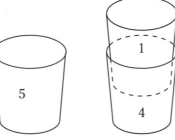

**67.** Put one marble in one box, three in another and five in a third one. Then place the three boxes inside the fourth box.

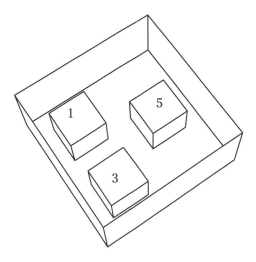

**68.** Take one marble from the box marked BW. If it is white, the other marble must also be white. This means that the box marked BB must have black and white marbles and the box marked WW must have only black marbles. You can apply the same principle if the first marble you take is black.

**69.** After being inverted twice, the hourglass continued working in its initial position. Therefore, the extra hour that it measured was a consequence of these two inversions, half an hour each time. If it was inverted for the second time at 11:30, the first time had to be a half-hour earlier, at 11:00.

**70.** The clock that doesn't work will show the precise time twice a day, but the fast one will take 2 × 60 × 12 = 1440 days to show the precise time. Therefore, the broken clock shows the correct time more often.

**71.** Time to have the clock fixed.

**72.** Ten times (you can verify it yourself).

**73.** Four seconds (it takes two seconds between 2 consecutive strikes).

**74.** Four hours, the time between 8 and 12.

**75.** There is 1 second between 2 strikes. Therefore, it will take 11 seconds for the clock to strike 12 times.

**76.** He lived 59 years, because there is no "0" year.

**77.** He would have drunk the same number of cups of coffee. The difference is that the conversation would have taken place on March 14.

**78.** Friday.

**79.** Three days and two nights. She left yesterday and will return tomorrow.

**80.** The man's birthday is December 31 and he was talking on January 1. He's 36 now, the day before yesterday he was 35, this calendar year he will turn 37, and next calendar year he will turn 38.

**81.** It happened to Gioacchino Rossini, who was born on February 29, 1792, and who died on November 13, 1868. Remember that 1800 was not a leap year. All years that are divisible by four are leap years, except those that end in "00." They are only leap years if they are divisible by 400.

**82.** INVENT.

**83.** Neither. The yolk of an egg is yellow.

**84.** It is not "I am going in" or "I am not going in." The opposite is "I am leaving."

**85.** The word "incorrectly."

**86.** Lounger.

**87.** It's a matter of language. Consider "four twenty" as $4.20. Then it is true.

**88.** Yes. "Paris" starts with a "p," and "ends" starts with an "e."

**89.** The phone operator was trying to get the spelling of the man's last name. Therefore it makes no sense to ask, "I as in what?" The operator had already understood it was an "I."

**90.** The letter "i."

**91.** Let's suppose it is false. By saying "This statement is false," it becomes true and vice versa. Therefore, to be false it has to be true and vice versa. It is a paradox.

**92.** The letter "u."

**93.** He will not change his mind.

**94.** His statement must be "I will be hanged." If they want to hang him, the sentence is true, and therefore, they will not be able to hang him. For the same reason, he cannot be drowned because his statement would be false and they could not drown him if his statement is false. (Based on *Don Quixote*, by Cervantes.)

**95.** Yes, as long as the other half are male, too. She has five sons.

**96.** Nine children.

**97.** Three more brothers than sisters. Ann's brother has one more brother than sister. Ann is one of the sisters, so Ann will have one fewer sister than her brother has and one more brother than her brother has.

**98.** Seven. The only possible solution is that the person talking is a woman and there are four women and three men.

**99.** The doctor is a woman.

**100.** John is Raymond's son.

**101.** Your mother.

**102.** The son's mother.

**103.** The second man is Charles's grandson.

**104.** No, because it would be his mother.

**105.** The man is Ann's uncle.

**106.** If the man left a widow, then he is dead. Therefore, he cannot get married.

**107.** She was looking at a photo of her nephew.

**108.** He was looking at a photo of his father.

**109.** Two widowers have one daughter each and decide to marry each other's daughters. This conversation takes place once they are married and with children. Their wives are the ones talking.

**110.** The Pacific Ocean. Even though it had not been discovered or named by Balboa, it was still the biggest ocean.

**111.** One cookie, because after eating one you would no longer have an empty stomach.

**112.** Because it wasn't raining.

**113.** Holes.

**114.** By walking and dragging the rope with it. The puzzle does not say that the leash is tied to something.

**115.** The number 400, to hang on a house. This number is formed by three digits, at $1 each.

**116.** It was daytime, so the room was light.

**117.** With one quarter and one nickel. The puzzle says that one of the coins is not a nickel, and it is true since a quarter is not a nickel.

**118.** Because he earns double by giving a haircut to two foreigners instead of to only one person in town.

**119.** He goes to the next room and by crawling toward the bottle, he slides into the room.

**120.** The plane had not yet taken off.

**121.** He had already put sugar in his coffee.

**122.** The match.

**123.** By serving mashed potatoes.

**124.** It is a male giraffe, so it is the father and not the mother of the offspring.

**125.** Ten cows. We can call the pigs cows, but it doesn't make them cows.

**126.** He must always be behind the whistle.

**127.** There is no reason to baptize him. If he is Catholic, he is already baptized.

**128.** The letter "e."

**129.** My uncle Emil is blind, and he was reading in Braille.

**130.** He is a farmer. He needs plenty of water, so if he lacks water he has no income and he won't be able to buy or even make wine.

**131.** At the beginning of the puzzle, it says that you are the cab driver. Therefore, the answer is your name and age.

**132.** One of the trains went into the tunnel hours after the other.

**133.** It was a girls' team.

**134.** My aunt Martha was a pedestrian, too.

**135.** The customers paid $27, $25 to cover their bill and $2 as a tip for the waiter.

**136.** The driver of the moped was the policeman's son.

**137.** The butcher's daughter is the fisherman's wife.

**138.** Since he's a butcher, he weighs meat.

**139.** The first four people pick one apple each, and the fifth one takes the basket with the apple in it.

**140.** Either a deep-sea diver or an astronaut.

**141.** "To sint" means to take off your clothes, and "to sant" is to go into the water to bathe.

**142.** Because before the game begins, the score is always 0-0.

**143.** I deposited $50 in my bank account to have enough funds to cash the check.

**144.** The passenger gave the driver 25 cents in the form of four nickels and five pennies.

**145.** Nine.

**146.** As far as half of the forest, because if she went any further, she would be leaving the forest, instead of going into it.

**147.** All the animals that have one, because as far as we know, no animal takes it off to eat.

**148.** You just have to light a match under a container with water.

**149.** Straight, arced, or spiral.

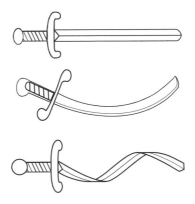

**150.** The parrot was deaf.

**151.** The surgeon was the boy's mother.

**152.** Because there are fewer black sheep than white sheep.

**153.** She dropped her earring into her coffee beans.

**154.** The dictionary. The word "foreword" comes before "epilogue," "end" is in the first half of the dictionary, and "index" comes before "introduction."

**155.** The girl's name is Anne COUPLE.

**156.** If it were an authentic coin, it could not have "b.c." (This system was created after Jesus died, not before he was born.)

**157.** Neither country, because they are survivors.

**158.** What the director actually needed was a real night shift guard that did not sleep at work, even if he could predict the future in his dreams.

**159.** My cousin Edward is bald. Therefore, his hair cannot get wet.

**160.** My aunt is really short and the button for the 25th floor is at the highest point she can reach.

**161.** The neighbor was snoring. That is why he couldn't sleep. When he made the call, the person woke up and stopped making noise.

**162.** He must turn on both faucets at the same time.

**163.** The woman died before the operation.

**164.** If three of the letters are correct, the fourth one must be too. Therefore, there is only one way.

**165.** The same month you are reading this.

**166.** The river was frozen.

**167.** When he sees his coworker, the miner with the clean face assumes that his face is also dirty and wipes it. The miner with a dirty face sees his coworker with a clean face and assumes that his is also clean.

**168.** The letter "g."

**169.** Hairdressers don't cut their own hair. Therefore, the clean hairdresser gave the bad haircut and the dirty hairdresser gave the perfect haircut. Thus, it is better to go to the dirty salon.

**170.** The customer was in his firefighter uniform.

**171.** Because in 96 hours it would again be night.

**172.** It was a drive-in theater. He killed her in the car. On his way out, nobody noticed that the woman was dead in the car.

**173.** First he immersed the crown in a container of water and measured the level of the water. Then he removed the crown and immersed the gold bar, measuring the water level. If the levels were not the same, the gold had been mixed with another metal.

**174.** Two apples.

**175.** It will still be 38°.

**176.** On his birthday.

**177.** He took the same time in both cases, because 1 hour and 20 minutes equals 80 minutes.

**178.** If the cab driver had been deaf, he would not have heard the address the passenger had given to him. He only mentioned he was deaf when the passenger didn't stop talking.

**179.** The waiter scared his customer, who had the hiccups. That is why the customer thanked the waiter.

**180.** If he became a widower when he was 55 and died when he was 80, he was a widower for 25 years.

**181.** One was standing at the main door of a bank and his friend was standing at the back door. There was 84 million dollars in the safe of the bank. Therefore, "between both of them" they had that amount of money.

**182.** I killed three flies. They remain. The rest would have flown away immediately.

**183.** By bending the match and then dropping it.

**184.** Drop it and catch it before it hits the ground.

**185.** Cutting it either of these ways:

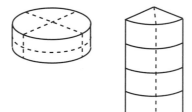

**186.** Tie the scissors to one of the ropes and make it move like a pendulum. Then take the other end of the rope and grab the scissors as they come toward you. Then tie the knot.

**187.** By gradually pouring sand into the hole. The bird will keep moving so that it is not buried in the sand, forcing it higher until it comes out.

**188.** He makes three cigarettes out of the nine cigarette butts. Every time he smokes one cigarette, he has one new cigarette butt. In total, he smokes four cigarettes and, therefore, smokes for four hours.

**189.** Cut it either of these ways:

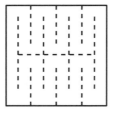 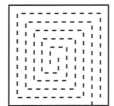

**190.** In two dimensions there is no solution, but it is possible in three dimensions, where you can form a tetrahedron.

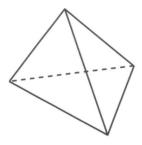

**191.** Oil floats in vinegar. All you have to do is to tilt the bottle. To pour vinegar, you have to turn the bottle upside down and by pulling off the cork a little, you can let the desired amount of vinegar out.

**192.** By placing it diagonally in a 30-by-30-inch package.

**193.** Cross your arms and hold a tip of the napkin in each hand. When you uncross your arms, the knot will be formed.

**194.** Yes, very easily, by folding the paper and then wrinkling it as shown below.

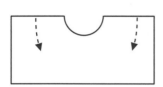 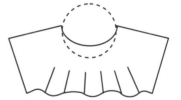

**195.** Make a knot with a loop at the base of the rope, and then cut the loop. The knot will be still holding the ends of the rope.

**196.** First, tie the lower ends. Then climb up the first rope and cut the second one, close to the ceiling, leaving an end long enough to form a loop. (You can instead cut it off entirely if you can slide the rope through the hook.) Hanging from the loop, cut the first rope at the hook. Be careful not to drop it. Then slide the rope through the loop until it's even. Climb down the double rope and, once on the floor, pull one end to get it all.

**197.** Pour water in the hole a little at a time. The ball will rise until it completely comes out of the hole.

**198.** By releasing some air from the tires so that they lower the total height of the truck more than two inches. The truck can then easily go under the bridge.

**199.** By tossing it upward. First it will go up, then it will stop momentarily and start coming down following the same path.

**200.** By cutting the wood into two or three pieces, 20 centimeters in length. In this way, you obtain pieces with a rectangular surface of 5 by 20 centimeters and you can then put them in the hole, stopping the leak.

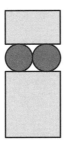 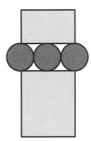

**201.** Yes, by putting on your pants inside-out.

**202.** When you take off your shoe, I'll take off mine at the same time. That way, you are not doing it alone.

**203.** By pushing the cork inside the bottle.

**204.** By turning the box upside down and sliding the lid enough to make some diamonds fall. Then close it, turn it back to its original position, and put it back in its place.

**205.** The paper reads, "You will write the word 'NO' on the paper." If you write "NO," you are indicating that it will not happen, although it has really happened. If you write "YES," you are indicating that it will happen, although it actually has not happened. No matter what you write, you will not get it right.

**206.** Save one penny every other day. When he dies, you will have the exact amount.

**207.** Place the newspaper page under a closed door. Each person steps on one end of the page so that they cannot touch each other without opening the door. To open the door, they would have to step off of the paper.

**208.** Something that specifically involves you. For example, crawling under your legs. Your friend can crawl under your legs, but you cannot crawl under your own legs.

**209.** Roll up the rug (or the bill) starting on one end until it reaches the bottle. Then, continue rolling it slowly so that the bottle moves until it is entirely off the rug. During this process, only the rug is touching the bottle.

**210.** Always advance half the distance remaining to the wall. In this way, there will always be some distance between you and the wall. The distance left approaches zero, but it never actually reaches zero.

If we consider d as the initial distance to the wall, the distance traveled is d $\times$ ($\frac{1}{2}$ + $\frac{1}{4}$ + $\frac{1}{8}$ + $\frac{1}{16}$ + ... + $\frac{1}{2^n}$).

**211.** Because they placed the ballpoint pen on the ground leaning against a high wall.

**212.** To make the authorities think that he was going to jump with a hostage. If they thought that, they would not give him a defective parachute.

**213.** There were no footprints. Therefore, the man and package fell from the sky. The package was the parachute that had not opened up. That is why the man was dead.

**214.** He was on a long bridge, so he had to run 20 yards toward where the police car was approaching from to get off the bridge. Then he ran toward the forest.

**215.** The husband died before he woke up. Therefore, nobody could have known what he had been dreaming about.

**216.** The man used the ladder to tie the rope to the hook. Then, he took it out of the room and brought in a big block of ice. He stood on the block of ice to hang himself. The moisture on the floor came from the ice melting down.

**217.** He talked to the travel agency where the couple had bought their tickets and found out that the husband had ordered a one-way ticket for his wife and a round-trip ticket for himself.

**218.** He took out one marble and swallowed it before someone else could see its color. This forced the count to take out the other marble. It was black, of course, so they all assumed that the previous one had been white.

**219.** He dug up the dirt with his hands to form a little mound. He then stepped on the mound to reach the water.

**220.** The man stabbed himself with an icicle. The ice melted. This explains why there was no weapon.

**221.** If Albert had stopped the cassette player when the killer came in, the tape would not have been rewound. This means that the killer had listened to the tape to make sure that the imitation was perfect.

**222.** The killer blocked the deadbolt with a chunk of ice. When the ice melted down, the door locked itself.

**223.** The maid, because pages 99 and 100 are two sides of the same sheet of paper.

**224.** If the police detective heard the shots at the same time, it means that the men could not have died at the same time. If both sounds had occurred at the same time at opposite ends of the train, he would have first heard the one from the front car, because the speed of the train was added to the speed of sound. For the sound from the back of the train, the speed of the train was subtracted from the speed of sound. For the detective to hear both shots at once means the man at the back of the train was killed first.

**225.** The guilty man was one conjoined twin, and his twin was innocent.

**226.** New York City is in the Northern Hemisphere and Australia is in the Southern Hemisphere. Due to the earth's movement, water and air masses turn in different directions in both hemispheres. In the Southern Hemisphere, they turn clockwise, while in the Northern Hemisphere, they turn counterclockwise. When he saw the direction of the water draining from the sink, he knew where he was.

**227.** The footprints were not very deep, which means that they could not belong to a very heavy person. Therefore, they had to belong to the secretary, who had changed shoes to hide her crime.

Both wounds must have occurred when the victim placed a hand on his chest before the gunshot and the bullet penetrated his hand before going into his chest.

**228.** I climbed up a cherry tree that had two cherries and picked only one. I left the other one on the tree. I did not "pick cherries," because I "picked a cherry."

**229.** Humans. When we are little, we crawl on all fours. When we are adults, we stand on two feet. When we are old, we use a cane.

**230.** Silence.

**231.** The letter "i."

**232.** A shadow.

**233.** None. The ship floats and it always weighs the same in the water. It will rise with the tide, so its flotation line will always be the same. So the ladder will still be 22 steps.

**234.** Two minutes. During the first minute, the front of the train will pass through the tunnel and during the second minute, the rest of the train will pass through the tunnel.

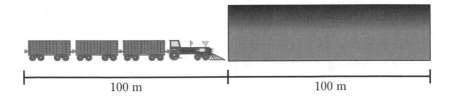

100 m          100 m

**235.** When they crossed, they were both in the same place. Therefore, they were both equidistant from Madrid.

**236.** The trains going to the movies arrive one minute earlier than the other ones. So if my uncle arrives at a random time, nine times out of ten the movie train will come first.

**237.** Two hours and thirteen minutes. (If you multiply by 60, the minutes become hours and the seconds become minutes.)

**238.** If you put my bird inside any airplane plane and make it fly in the same direction as the plane, it will be going faster than the plane.

**239.** The top of the highest mast in the boat traveled a distance $2\varpi d$ feet longer than the lowest point of the boat, which is d feet lower.

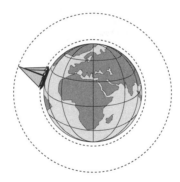

**240.** A bird cannot fly on the moon because there is no air to suspend it.

**241.** The passenger should sit at the end of the train and when the train enters the tunnel, he should run toward the front of the train. The time he spends in the tunnel will be shorter than if he had remained seated.

**242.** The combined speed of the trains is 50 + 70 = 120 miles per hour. It will take them half an hour to travel the 60 miles between them. During this time, the bird will travel 40 miles.

**243.** 100 inches. The stone moves relative to the log and the log to the terrain.

**244.** The combined speed of the trains is 80 + 120 = 200 meters per minute. One minute before crashing, they will be 200 meters apart.

**245.** You might think that the snail would take 200 minutes in traveling 100 centimeters, but you have to realize that at the end of the 194th minute it will be three centimeters away from the end. This means that in the 195th minute, the snail will reach it and will not slide down again. The answer is 195 minutes.

**246.** The young man took ten minutes to go to the other end of the train and back. During this time, the man's suitcases have traveled five miles. The train travels five miles every ten minutes, which makes the speed 30 miles per hour.

**247.** Fifteen, counting the times that they meet at a port while one ship is leaving and the other arriving. Thirteen, if we do not count these crossings. When the ship leaves, there are already seven ships on the way that it will come across at some point during the journey. It will also cross with the one ship that leaves when it leaves and the seven other ships that will depart during the ship's journey. The figure below represents this situation. The arrow indicates a ship that leaves New York destined for London. The dotted lines indicate the ships it passes.

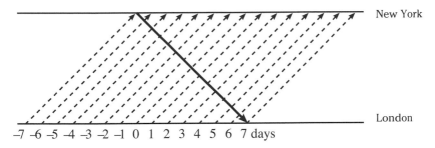

**248.** The needle will travel approximately 9.5 centimeters (the radius of the record minus the non-playable areas, $15 - 5 - 0.5 = 9.5$ centimeters.) Actually, the speed of the record and the number of grooves do not affect the result. The needle moves in an arc of a circle whose radius is the length of the tonearm.

**249.** This point maintains a constant speed, independent of the length of the shadow.

**250.** When the car speeds up, the inertia pushes the air back inside the car, compressing the air behind the balloon and thus pushing the balloon forward. When the car turns, the balloon will move toward the inside of the turn.

**251.** The lower ends of the rim of the wheels. Their trajectory is shown below:

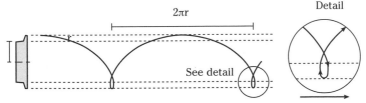

When the train goes in one direction, those points move in the opposite direction.

**252.** If the dog went faster than 330 meters per second (the speed of sound), it could not hear the noise of the can. So that is the fastest the dog can run.

**253.** Because the speed ratio was the same, runner number "1" won. We can verify this mathematically:

$$V_1/V_2 = {}^{100}/_{95} = {}^{105}/_{x_2}$$
$$x_2 = 99.75 \text{ meters}$$

**254.** The director got to the office 20 minutes early and he saw the car at "x" distance from his house. Then the car takes 20 minutes in traveling that distance back and forth. So the director came across the car 10 minutes before his regular departure time and therefore he walked exactly 50 minutes.

**255.** Without the current, the boat takes 20 minutes. It goes six miles in twenty minutes, so its speed is 18 mph.

With a current, the first trip would be $V_1 = 18 - 2 = 16$ mph, taking $T_1 = {}^{D_1}/_{V_1} = {}^{3}/_{16} = 11$ minutes and 15 seconds. The return trip would be $V_2 = 18 + 2 = 20$ mph, taking $T_2 = {}^{3}/_{20} = 9$ minutes.

The total trip, in this case, would take 20 minutes and 15 seconds, which is more than the trip without the current.

**256.** There is such a spot. Let's imagine that on the same day that one person was climbing down, the other one was climbing up. They must have met at a certain point of the trip. This is the spot we are looking for.

**257.** Two blankets one inch thick each, because the air between them also acts as insulation.

**258.** No. It hasn't because the total weight of the ice is equal to the volume of water displaced.

**259.** This can never happen. These are two contradictory concepts. If one of them exists, the other cannot possibly exist as well.

**260.** At the North or South Pole.

**261.** I must pour it before going upstairs, because the coffee will lose more heat before adding the milk rather than after. (Matter loses heat proportionally to the difference in temperature with the surrounding environment.)

**262.** The flotation line will be lower, because the raft will be lighter. The water level of the pool will also be lower, because the volume of water that the rocks displace when they are in the raft is larger than the volume of water the rocks displace when they are at the bottom of the pool. When the rocks are on the raft, they displace a volume of water equal to the weight of the rocks. When the rocks are at the bottom of the pool, the volume of the water displaced is equal to the actual volume of the rocks. Since rocks are denser than water, this is the smaller of the two volumes.

**263.** The flotation line will be the same, because the weight of the boat does not change.

**264.** Eight times, as shown below.

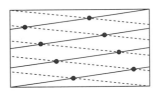

**265.** While the raft is loaded with the salt, he must mark the flotation line. Then, he must unload the salt and load the raft with gold until the water level reaches the flotation line. This means that the weight of the salt and the gold will be equal.

**266.** Place the bottle horizontally and let the wine gradually pour out until the horizontal surface of the wine is at the middle of the bottle, as shown in the illustration.

**267.** Put pieces of glass of the broken pitcher in the pitcher containing acid until the level reaches the five-quart mark. Then pour the acid until it reaches the two-quart mark.

**268.** Before leaving home, he wound the clock and set it for 12:00. When he got back home, he knew exactly how long he had been out because of his own clock.

At his friend's house, he checked the time. Once he was back home, he subtracted the time he was at his friend's house from the total time indicated by the clock. The remainder was used in walking to and from his friend's house. He divided this number into two and added the result to the time that he saw on his friend's clock when he was leaving his friend's house.

**269.** Two turns on itself. (You can actually try this yourself.)

**270.** Mr. Brown does not wear a brown or white tie. Therefore, it has to be red. Mr. White's tie can't be white, so it must be brown. That leaves Mr. Red with the white tie.

**271.** The maximum distance for the first two points is when they are on opposite ends of a circumference of that sphere. The circumference divides the sphere in two hemispheres. The third point has to be in one of these hemispheres. Therefore, it will certainly happen.

**272.** The puzzle says to draw a square "with two straight lines." The easiest solution is the one shown in the illustration below, which shows a square with two straight lines.

**273.** It is possible to predict it. That doesn't mean that he is right in his predictions.

**274.** This puzzle is based on an old joke. What really happened was that the young man kissed his own hand and then slapped the older man in the face.

**275.** There is no smoke coming out of an electric train.

**276.** Peacocks don't lay eggs. Peahens do.

**277.** A hole, for example.

**278.** One dozen.

**279.** He has a glass eye.

**280.** A quintet.

**281.** When he got married, he was a billionaire. Because of his wife's spending habits, he became a millionaire.

**282.** He can take out his dentures and bite his good eye with them.

**283.** Baby elephants.

**284.** During his last lap.

**285.** You can go in through the door.

**286.** The hare was lying. (The first paragraph of the puzzle gives the order.)

**287.** Staying up at night.

**288.** Wet.

**289.** Bicycles.

**290.** Construct a chart to consider the possible values.

| E | 1 | 2 | 3 | 4 | 5 | 6 | 7 | 8 | 9 |
|---|---|---|---|---|---|---|---|---|---|
| Carryovers | | | 1 | 1 | 2 | 2 | 2 | 3 | 3 |
| N | 4 | 8 | 2 | 6 | 0 | 4 | 8 | 2 | 6 |
| 4N + Carryovers | 6 | 2 | 9 | 5 | 2 | 8 | 4 | 1 | 7 |

E cannot equal zero since that would make N zero. We need a value where four E's equal N and four N's are equal to E plus a carryover. From the chart, we see that the only place where that occurs is when E equals 2. Therefore, E = 2, N = 8, and O must equal 1, since any number greater than that would result in an additional carryover.

$$
\begin{array}{r}
182 \\
182 \\
182 \\
+182 \\
\hline
728
\end{array}
$$

**291.** When referring to columns, they are numbered from left to right. In the first column, N + M + S is equal to a number less than 10. Therefore, the greatest number of the three could be a 6 with no carryover from the second column, or a 5 with a carryover from the second column. Obviously, there is a carryover from, or to, at least one of the two middle columns, since their sums yield two different letters.

Let's make an assumption that there is a carryover to the first column, and, therefore, no number can be greater than 5 in that column.

Now consider the possibilities for the last column.

| N | 1 | 2 | 3 | 4 | 5 |
|---|---|---|---|---|---|
| Carryovers | | | | 1 | 1 |
| E | 3 | 6 | 9 | 2 | 5 |

N cannot equal 5, because then E would equal 5. If N = 1, O would have to be 7, which is impossible, since the sum of the second column would then be 23. If N = 3, then O = 1 and U must also be 3, which is impossible. N cannot equal 4 because that would mean that O would equal 1, and both remaining numbers in the first column would be greater than 4. Therefore, N equals 2 and E equals 6.

If N is 2, then O must be 4. Since we accounted for the numbers 2, 3, and 4, M + S can only equal 1 and 5, and they are interchangeable.

```
  2442              2442
  5442              1442
 +1442             +5442
  9326              9326
```

**292.** Here are three solutions. Can you find others?

```
  8026        8096        8096
    26          96          96
   938         748         758
 +1280       +1980       +1980
 10270       10920       10930
```

**293.** Since A + B = Z and Z + P = T, it follows that A + B + P = T. We also know that T + A = F, so adding the last two equations and simplifying, we get 2A + B + P = F. We know that B + P + F = 24, so we have:

$$24 - B - P = F$$
$$\underline{2A + B + P = F}$$
$$24 + 2A = 2F \text{ or } 12 + A = F$$

We can replace F with T + A. The equation then becomes 12 + A = T + A, so T = 12 and therefore Q = 19.

**294.** View C is not correct.

**295.** Besides the three shown in this puzzle, eight other ways are possible.

**296.** It is always helpful to set up a legend of what is given and to work from there.

$$X = \$.50 \text{ pens}$$
$$Y = \$5.50 \text{ pens}$$
$$Z = \$9.50 \text{ pens}$$

Set up two equations as follows:

$$X + Y + Z = 100$$
$$\$.50X + \$5.50Y + \$9.50Z = 100$$

Now, we need at least one of the values to drop out in order to consider the other two. Multiply the first equation by $-.5$ to drop X out of both equations.

$$
\begin{aligned}
-0.5X \quad -0.5Y \quad -0.5Z &= -50 \\
+0.5X \quad +5.5Y \quad +9.5Z &= 100 \\
\hline
+5.0Y \quad +9.0Z &= 50
\end{aligned}
$$

$$5Y = 50 - 9Z$$
$$Y = 10 - \frac{9}{5}Z$$

Since we're dealing with whole numbers, Z must be a whole number and a multiple of 5. In this case, Z can only equal 5. With any greater number, Y will become a negative number. So, Z = 5 and Y becomes 1, leaving X to be 94 pens at $.50.

94 pens at $.50
1 pen at $5.50
5 pens at $9.50

**297.** B, C, and D form the triangle.

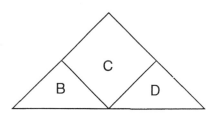

**298.** Q, K, Q, Q, K, K, and K is the order that works.

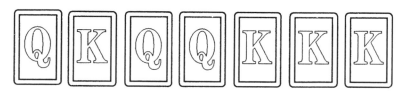

**299.**

  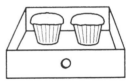

As you can see, there are only three possibilities where a chocolate cupcake could be chosen first.

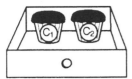 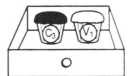 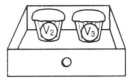

Out of these three, there are only two where a chocolate cupcake could be chosen second.

The answer is two out of three.

**300.** If the first digit of the four-digit code cannot be 0, 5, or 7, that leaves seven possible numbers for the first digit. All ten digits, however, can be used for the second, third, and fourth numbers.

$7 \times 10 \times 10 \times 10$

There are 7,000 possible different codes.

**301.** Columns are numbered from left to right. There has to be a carryover of 2 to the first column. If P were 9 and Q were 8, with a carryover of 1 from the last column, the sum of 20 could not be reached if R equaled 1. Therefore, R cannot be 1.

**302.** The powers of 7 have a repeating pattern for the last digit that can be found easily without performing the entire multiplication of each power.

$$7^0 \quad 7^1 \quad 7^2 \quad 7^3 \quad 7^4 \quad 7^5 \quad 7^6 \quad 7^7$$

$$1 \quad 7 \quad 9 \quad 3 \quad 1 \quad 7 \quad 9 \quad 3$$

With a repeating pattern of four, $7^{32}$ has the same remainder as $7^0$, which is 1. Then $7^{33}$ would be in the next column, $7^1$. Its remainder is 7 when divided by 10.

**303.** This type of puzzle is a form of syllogism. It can best be shown by using Venn diagrams.

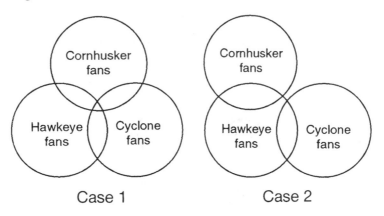

Case 1          Case 2

From Case 1, we can see that it is possible for a Cornhusker to be a Cyclone fan, but from Case 2, it is not definite. The conclusion is false.

**304.** Obviously, their number system is based on something other than 10. Let's say it is based on a notation represented by N.

3N + 0, their number 30, is the number we call 24.

You can reason that 3N + 0 = 24, and N = 8.

Likewise, 3N + 4 = 28, and N = 8.

Their number system is then $BASE_8$ and $5 \times 4 \times 7$, our 140, becomes their 214.

| $8^2$ | $8^1$ | $8^0$ |
|---|---|---|
| 2 | 1 | 4 |

**305.** Since Dave spoke to the biologist, and Ann was sitting next to the chemist and across from the doctor, Cathy must be the author, and Ann is the biologist. The doctor didn't speak, but Dave did. So, Boobie is the doctor (and was thinking of her own parents) and Dave is the chemist.

**306.** Turn the first grid 90° to the right, and delete the bottom row of figures. Then turn the result 90° to the right again and delete the bottom row. Do the same with the third grid to get the answer.

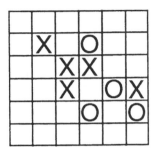

**307.** The sum is ⅓. Can you determine what the sum is of the infinite series ⅓ + ⅑ + 1/27 + 1/81 . . . ?

**308.** You can approach this puzzle in several ways.

REBRAG = ◇
◇
○
○
○

LEG = ◇ ◇ ◇

One of the first things you may have noticed is that the horizontal figures both contain an L, whereas the two vertical figures contain an R. The equations with two figures both contain a B and the equations with three figures both have a G. The circles have an A and the diamonds an E for their lone vowels. So, that yields this basic information.

L = horizontal     B = 2
R = vertical       A = ○
G = 3              E = ◇

**309.** In the first two foreign phrases, roi is the only common word. The word "three" in the English version is likewise the only common word; so, roi means "three." In the second and third foreign phrases, the word kir is used. The English translations share the word meaning "coins." So, kir means coins. Comparing the first and third phrases, we see they share the word kaf, meaning "take." Therefore, kaf means "take." From the English translation of the first phrase, "Kaf navcki roi," we know that navcki means "pieces." From the second phrase, palt must mean "hide," and from the third phrase, inoti means "cautiously."

"Hide pieces cautiously" becomes "Palt navcki inoti," assuming that the foreign syntax follows that of English.

**310.** The probability is 14.3 percent. Twenty-two percent of the people are not gum chewers and 65 percent are over fifteen years old. Therefore, 22 percent $\times$ 65 percent, or 14.3 percent, are not gum chewers and are above the age of fifteen.

**311.** The only relationship these capital letters have is that their shapes are totally or partially closed. R is the next and last letter of the alphabet that meets this requirement.

**312.** The answer is "A is larger than B by 1." This is a good example of reducing a seemingly difficult problem to an example that is workable.

For instance, $2^5 = 32$.

$2^4(16) + 2^3(8) + 2^2(4) + 2^1(2) + 2^0(1) = 31$

That is 1 less than 32.

**313.** It only took John four steps to accomplish his task.

Step 1—John filled the five-gallon bucket and poured all of it into the six-gallon bucket.

Step 2—He refilled the five-gallon bucket and poured out one gallon into the six-gallon bucket to fill it, leaving four gallons in the five-gallon bucket.

Step 3—He dumped the six-gallon bucket and poured the four gallons from the five-gallon bucket into the six-gallon bucket.

Step 4—Then, John refilled the five-gallon bucket and started home for a piece of cake.

**314.** The answer is 6119. These four numbers read the same right side up as they do upside down. The numbers on the right are the ones that most closely follow the ones on the left.

**315.** EMIT spelled backwards is TIME. STAR spelled backwards is RATS.

**316.** The next number is 4. Here's how to set up the problem.

If the difference of the numbers of the series is taken to the end, a pattern of −3 is established. The next number in the series must yield a −3 in the bottom row. The number next to −8 must be −11. Next to −6 is a −17, and 4 is next to 21.

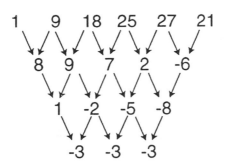

So, here's how we complete the diagram of the setup.

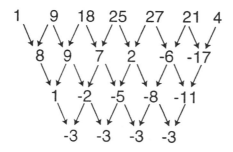

**317.** In one day, nine men work at a rate of X compared to seven women who work at a rate of Y. This can be expressed as:

$$5(9X + 7Y)$$

Likewise in the second case:

$$4(7X + 11Y)$$

Since these two amounts are equal, we have the following equation:

$$5(9X + 7Y) = 4(7X + 11Y)$$

$$45X + 35Y = 28X + 44Y$$

$$17X = 9Y$$

$$\frac{Y \text{ or women's rate}}{X \text{ or men's rate}} = \frac{17}{9}$$

The women are better workers by a ratio of 17 to 9.

**318.** The next number is 224. Notice that no digit is greater than 4. That's because these are the $BASE_{10}$ numbers 1, 2, 4, 8, 16, 32, and 64 converted to numbers in $BASE_5$.

**319.** The missing number is 1. This is the fraction $\frac{1}{7}$ converted to decimal form.

**320.** The number is 8. Starting with the first and last numbers and working towards the middle, each pair of numbers totals 20.

**321.** The next number is 30. This is actually two different series contained within one. One series begins with 0 and continues with every other number. Likewise, starting with the 2, a second series is established with every other number.

**322.** The missing number is 5. Each number stands for a letter of the alphabet where A = 1, B = 2, C = 3, etc. The word spelled out is PUZZLES.

**323.** The answer is 51. In this problem, the differences between the numbers forms a pattern, allowing you to predict the next numbers. After finding the difference, find the difference of the resulting numbers.

**324.** The correct number is 51. These numbers represent the answers for each of the six problems starting with Puzzle 318.

**325.** Unscrambled, the letters spell out ALBERT EINSTEIN.

**326.** The maximum number of cubes is nineteen.

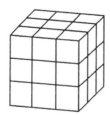

**327.** There are several different methods of approaching this problem. Since there are three unknowns, it is helpful to establish whatever relationship may exist between the unknowns and then attempt to express that relationship in common terms.
Looking at the first two parts of the equations, we see that § = 2⊗.
We know that ¶ – § = 6 and, therefore, § = ¶ – 6, which means that 2⊗ = ¶ – 6.
If we replace each § with 2⊗, we then have 7⊗ = 2¶.
Solving for ≤ in the third equation, we have ⊗ = $\dfrac{¶ - 6}{2}$.

Solving for ⊗ in the fourth equation, we have $\otimes = \dfrac{2\P}{7}$.

$$\dfrac{\P - 62}{2} = \dfrac{2}{7} \qquad 3\P = 42$$
$$7(\P - 6) = 4\P \qquad \P = 14$$
$$7\P - 42 = 4\P \qquad \S = 8$$
$$\otimes = 4$$

**328.** Each X moves clockwise on the outside squares. Each O moves counterclockwise.

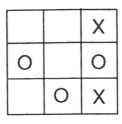

**329.** From several thousand feet high, the pyramid would look like this. The 60° angle between Lines A and B would appear to be 90° to Judy.

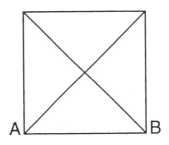

**330.** Rendrag paid $120 for the entire trip, so for the half of the trip the students were traveling, Rendrag paid $60.00. For the price to be mathematically equitable, the students would each pay $20 to Rendrag for a total of $40. Rendrag's portion for this part of the trip is $20 also.

**331.** Think of the two figures as an opaque rectangle that has an opaque square behind it. To arrive at the second part of the analogy, the square (the bottom figure) rotates 45° in either direction, and the rectangle (the top figure) rotates 90° in either direction.

To find the correct solution, rotate the rectangle (now the bottom figure) 45°, and rotate the square (now the top figure) 90°. The answer is C.

**332.** Consider the first figure in the analogy to be two transparent triangles sharing a common base. Let the triangle on the left flip downwards, using the base as an axis. This will give you the second figure. Likewise, in the third figure, let the line connected to the circle on the left fall around the base. C is the answer.

**333.** A cube is made up of six planes; a tetrahedron has four planes. A triangle has three planes, so it needs two lines to keep it in the same 6 to 4 (3 to 2) ratio. Only A works.

**334.** In the first two figures of the analogy, place the vertical line of the second figure directly behind the vertical line of the first. Where two flags meet on the same side of the line, they turn into a square on the third figure. Where a flag and a circle meet, they cancel each other out, and no figure appears. If flags or circles are unopposed, they appear as they are on their respective sides of the combined lines. The result is:

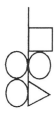

**335.** C is the only figure that can't be completed with one continuous line that does not retrace any part of the figure.

**336.** Think it's impossible? It can be done.

The northbound train pulls into the siding, leaving its tail end hanging out on the main track. Meanwhile, the southbound train stays beyond the north switch of the siding, on the main track. When the northbound train stops just short of Point Z (in railroad terms, "in the clear of the main track"), the crew signals the southbound train to proceed south on the main track.

After the southbound train has pulled down fifty or sixty cars, it stops. At Point Z, one of its crew members makes a cut on the fifty or so cars of the southbound train. The southbound train pulls far enough down the main track to allow the northbound train to get out of the siding. The southbound train will have enough room to pull down and not interfere with the cars from the northbound train that are still on the main track.

The crew from the northbound train lines the switch at the top end of the siding, and the northbound train proceeds north, coupling its engine onto the remaining cars of the southbound train. It shoves north, leaving the siding completely. A member of the southbound train's crew lines the bottom end of the siding switch for the main track, and the southbound train pulls its car down two miles or so and stops. Another crew member lines the switch at the top end of the siding for the main track.

The northbound train proceeds south. The engine is pushing its 100 cars and pulling the remaining cars from the southbound train. When the northbound train (now traveling south) gets all its cars past the bottom or southern end of the siding, it lines the siding switch and shoves the remaining cars from the southbound train into the siding. When it comes back out, a crew member lines the switch for the main track, and the train proceeds north with its entire train intact.

The southbound train shoves back to the siding, picks up its remaining cars, and heads south with its entire train. (Hopefully, the crew of the southbound train will line the bottom siding switch for the main track after they pull out, so the next train won't have an open siding switch to worry about.)

**337.** Border patrol

**338.** Good with numbers

**339.** Since Gear R has to make a complete trip around both fixed gears, it doesn't make any difference where we begin. For clarity's sake, we'll start as shown here.

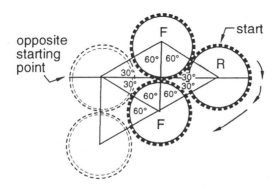

Keep in mind that if Gear R were to revolve around only the top fixed gear, it would make two revolutions, since their diameters are the same. Therefore, Gear R will make one revolution when it reaches the position of the lower left dashed circle.

In order for Gear R to continue to a position opposite its starting point, it needs to travel 60° more, as shown. Since 60°/180° = $\frac{1}{3}$, Gear R makes an additional $\frac{1}{3}$ revolution, for a total of $1\frac{1}{3}$ revolutions to its halfway point. Multiply that by 2 for the whole rotation, and you find that the answer is $2\frac{2}{3}$ revolutions.

**340.** The question asks for rates. These are usually expressed in units of time, in this case, miles per hour. We are not really interested in the fact that Sara may have traveled two or more hours, because her rate will always be the same.

In one hour, Sara will travel 4 miles down the river. Coming back, against the current, she must travel the same 4 miles, but it will take her two hours to accomplish this. In order to get a rate for one hour, we have to find out how far she traveled against the current in one hour, and that is 2 miles.

Sara travels a total of 6 miles in two hours for a rate of 3 mph. Since she has gone up and down the river, the rate of the river is cancelled out, and Sara's rate is 3 mph (6 miles divided by two hours) in still water, which means the rate of the river is 1 mph.

**341.** Candace is Jane's niece.

**342.** In a twelve-hour period starting after either 6 a.m. or 6 p.m., there will be eleven times when the hands are directly opposite each other. Twelve hours divided by eleven equals 1 hour, 5 minutes, and $27\frac{3}{11}$ seconds. Go back the 1 hour, 5 minutes, and $27\frac{3}{11}$ seconds from 6 o'clock, and you get 4:54 and $32\frac{8}{11}$ seconds.

**343.** The missing letter is R. The letters spell out "What is the answer?"

**344.** The sum of the three numbers below the diameter equals $\frac{1}{3}$ of the top number. So, the answer is one.

**345.** Ten weights will balance either 50 gold coins or 40 silver coins. Since only 20 gold coins are used, that means the weight of 30 gold coins is to be used by the silver coins. The weights are in a 4-to-5 ratio, and $\frac{4}{5}$ of 30 = 24. So, 24 silver coins should be added to the 20 gold coins to balance the 10 weights.

**346.** Here are the answers.
   A = 3
   B = 1
   C = 4
   D = 2

**347.** The 2-inch hose will drain the water faster, since it has a bigger spout area than the two 1-inch hoses. The area of a circle is given by multiplying $\pi$ (3.14) times the radius squared. The radius of the 2-inch hose is 1 inch. Its area is equal to $\pi \times 1 \times 1$ or $\pi$ square inches. The area of the two 1-inch hoses is:

$$\pi \times \tfrac{1}{2} \times \tfrac{1}{2} + \pi \times \tfrac{1}{2} \times \tfrac{1}{2}$$

or $\pi/4 + \pi/4$, which equals $\pi/2$ square inches

The 2-inch hose drains water twice as fast.

**348.**

$$
\begin{array}{r}
41067 \\
\underline{41607} \\
\$826743
\end{array}
$$

**349.**

$$
\begin{array}{rr}
6 & 2174 \\
\underline{+\,6} & \underline{2980} \\
12 & 5154
\end{array}
$$

**350.** The numbers are the numbers on the telephone, as shown here.

| ABC | DEF | GHI | JKL | MNO | PRS | TUV | WXY |
|-----|-----|-----|-----|-----|-----|-----|-----|
| 2 | 3 | 4 | 5 | 6 | 7 | 8 | 9 |

If the number is slanted to the left, then the left-most letter of that grouping is the letter to be used. If it is slanted to the right, the right-most letter is the choice. Letters that are straight up and down are represented by the center letter.

The note says, "Went to buy a new phone."

**351.** If 81 students had taken a course in geography, then only 9 students out of the 90 (10 took neither) took only geology. Since 63 students out of 90 had taken geology, that leaves 27 who had taken only geography.

$27 + 9 = 36$      $36/100$ is 36 percent

The answer is 36 percent or nine out of twenty-five.

Since 36 students took either geography or geology and 10 took neither, that leaves 54 percent who took at least one class in both.

**352.** Unfinished Symphony

**353.** Although the chances are remote, you just might pull the 24 blue socks out first. You'd need two more to make certain to get two black socks. You'd be assured of a pair of black socks by pulling 26 socks.

**354.** The first two digits enclosed within any parentheses are added together to get the second number contained within each parentheses. To get the first two digits of any following parentheses, add the numbers found in the preceding parentheses together. In this case, that is:

**37:10**

**355.** Dashing through the snow

**356.** Let's take a look at how this might be accomplished. Each letter represents a different person present at the gathering. Remember that when one person shakes another's hand, each person gets credit for a handshake. There are several ways to accomplish this. Here's one.

X shakes hands with W, Y, Z, T.
Y shakes hands with W, Z, T, X.
W shakes hands with Z, T, X, Y.
Z shakes hands with R, X, Y, W.
T shakes hands with S, X, Y, W.

As can be seen from our chart, X, Y, W, Z, and T each have four handshakes. R and S each have one. So the minimum number of people needed to accomplish the required handshakes is seven. X, Y, W, Z, and T each have four handshakes, and R and S have one apiece for a total of twenty-two handshakes.

**357.** Below is a table showing different combinations and probabilities of the dice. From the total combinations, we can see that there are a total of thirty-six chances.

| Total Number Showing on Dice | Total Combinations | Chances |
|---|---|---|
| 2 | 1 | 1/36 |
| 3 | 2 | 2/36 |
| 4 | 3 | 3/36 |
| 5 | 4 | 4/36 |
| 6 | 5 | 5/36 |
| 7 | 6 | 6/36 |
| 8 | 5 | 5/36 |
| 9 | 4 | 4/36 |
| 10 | 3 | 3/36 |
| 11 | 2 | 2/36 |
| 12 | 1 | 1/36 |

You can see there are three ways to roll a 10 and six ways to roll a 7. Out of these nine possibilities, three are favorable for a win. Therefore, the chances for winning with 10 as a point are one in three.

**358** Let's work this out.

Obviously, 10 must be in the top row, but it cannot be in either of the first two positions, since that would result in a duplication of 5's. Since 7 can only result from either 8 − 1 or 9 − 2, 8 and 9 must be in the top or next row. Nine can only result from 10 − 1, or it has to be in the top row. Therefore, 8 and 9 are not in the same row, and neither are 1 and 2, but all four numbers are in the top two rows. Out of the seven positions in the top two rows, we have 10, 9, 8, 1, 2, and 5 with 7 in the third row. That leaves 6, 3, or 4 for the remaining position in the top row. The digit next to the 7 can't be a 6 because that would result in duplicate 1's, and 6 cannot be the result of 7 minus any other number. Therefore, 6 is the remaining number of the seven numbers in the top two rows.

Six cannot be next to 5 or above 7, so it must be in the top row with 10. But 6 cannot be next to 10, so it is in the first or second position of the top row. And the number next to it must be 1. That means 9 cannot be in the top row; it would have to be next to 10, which would result in double 1's when subtracted. Eight must then be the other number in the top row.

That means the top row is 6  1  10  8, from which the remaining numbers can be generated:

$$
\begin{array}{cccc}
6 & 1 & 10 & 8 \\
 & 5 & 9 & 2 \\
 & & 4 & 7 \\
 & & 3 &
\end{array}
$$

For numbers 1 through 15:

$$
\begin{array}{ccccc}
13 & 3 & 15 & 14 & 6 \\
 & 10 & 12 & 1 & 8 \\
 & & 2 & 11 & 7 \\
 & & & 9 & 4 \\
 & & & 5 &
\end{array}
$$

**359.** The two winning first moves are these.

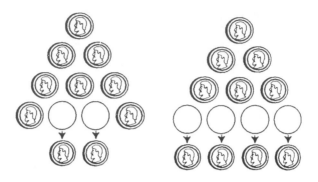

**360.** Here's one way the letter cross could look.

4265

8

3

1790

The total of the numbers used is 51 (17 × 3). The total of the numbers 1 through 9 is 45. There is a difference of 6. That difference is found in the letters D and G, since they are the only two letters counted twice. D and G must equal 6, and E + F must equal 11 to total 17 in the column. Since A = 4, D and G must be 1 and 5. The number 7 cannot be E or F. It would require the 4 to total 11. Also, 7 cannot be B, C, or D, since 4 + 7 would require the remaining two numbers in the top row to total 6, which is impossible. Therefore, 7 is in the bottom row with 0. That means the bottom row needs two numbers (besides 7 and 0) to total 10 for G + H + I + J to equal 17. One of those numbers must be 1 or 5. It can't be 5. You'd then have two 5's to total 10. Therefore, D = 5, G = 1, and the remaining number in the bottom row is 9. At this point the puzzle looks like this.

4BC5

E

F

1790

E + F must equal 11. The possible combinations are as follows.

2 + 9

3 + 8

4 + 7

5 + 6

The only possibility out of this group is 3 + 8, solving the values for D, E, F, and G, leaving 6 and 2 for B and C.

**361.** The next one is 46656.

Disregarding the number 1, these are the four consecutive lowest numbers that are both cubes and squares.

| 64 | 729 | 4,096 |
|:---:|:---:|:---:|
| $8^2$ or $4^3$ | $27^2$ or $9^3$ | $64^2$ or $16^3$ |
| **15,625** | and the fifth, | **46,656** |
| $125^2$ or $25^3$ | | $216^2$ or $36^3$ |

**362.** Here's how to find the answer.

Since we know that Box C isn't the smallest, out of Boxes A, B, C, and D, Box D is the smallest. Its number is either 4 or 5.

The possible numbers for Box C are 2, 3, or 4 (not the largest or the smallest).

Box A can only be 2 or 3, since it is bigger than Box C or Box D, but it is not the biggest.

The total of Box C plus Box D must be at least 6 but not more than 7. The greatest possible sum of two different numbers between 1 and 5 is 7, assuming that sum is the equal to the sum of two other different numbers.

Since Box A is 2 or 3, and its number plus Box E's number must be at least 6, Box E is either 4 or 5.

Box A = 2 or 3
Box C = 2 or 3
Box D = 4 or 5
Box E = 4 or 5

We know that Box A is bigger than Box C, so Box A = 2, Box C = 3, Box D = 4, Box E = 5, and Box B = 1.

**363.** Three out of eight chances. Here are the possibilities.

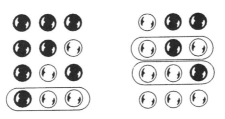

So, there are only three chances out of the eight possible combinations you could make.

**364.** Believe it or not, fifteen pieces (maximum) will result with four straight cuts through a cube.

This formula will give you the answer for any number of cuts. N = the number of cuts. So, three planar cuts yield eight pieces, four planar cuts yield fifteen pieces, five planar cuts yield twenty-six pieces, and six planar cuts yield forty-two pieces, and so on.

$$\left( \frac{N3 + 5N}{6} \right)_{+1} = \text{Number of Pieces}$$

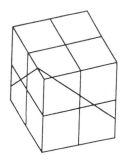

**365.** Let's see how its done. You only need to move five coins to turn the triangle upside down.

1—Move 3 to Row 3, outside 4.

2—Move 2 to Row 3, outside 6.

3—Move 1 to Row 6, between 12 and 13.

4—Move 15 to Row 6, between 13 and 14.

5—Move 11 to be the lone coin on the point of the upside-down triangle.

In general, where N is equal to the length of any side of a triangle (length in number of coins), the minimum number of coins that need to be moved to turn that triangle upside down can be found by this formula.

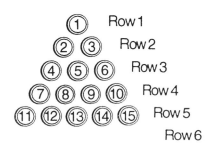

$$\frac{N\,(N+1)}{6}$$

If the result of the division has a remainder, the answer is simply rounded down to the nearest whole number found in the quotient.

For example, if N = 7, then $\frac{7 \times 8}{6}$ = 6 $\overline{)56}$ = 9.

Rounding down to 9 will give the minimum number of coins needed to be moved in a triangle that has seven coins on a side.

Special thanks to mathematician Frank Bernhart (Rochester, N.Y.) for his assistance.

**366.** Here are the remaining moves.

> 7—Move 1 to 4.
> 8—Move 15 to 6.
> 9—Move 6 to 13.
> 10—Move 12 to 14.
> 11—Move 4 to 13.
> 12—Move 14 to 12.
> 13—Move 11 to 13.

**367.** Regardless of which face of Cube 1 you start with, the tunnel cannot exit through Cubes 3, 5, or 8.

**368.** This object requires six cubes to build. Here is its orthographic projection and the sixth side.

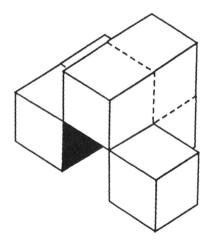
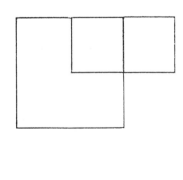

**369.** A man among men

**370.** Here's one way.

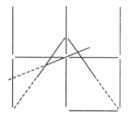

**371.** Far be it from me

**372.** If you are not careful, this short logic puzzle can be very confusing. Often, a solver's first instinct is to compare the speed and strength of each of the friends to determine their nicknames. Further inspection reveals that there isn't enough information to solve the puzzle that way. Here's where a grid of possibilities comes in handy.

We'll use X's and O's to fill in the grids. O will represent an elimination, and X will be a definite selection.

From a, we know that Pat can't be either Rabbit or Fly. So he must be either Bear or Walleye. We know from b that Tom cannot be either Rabbit or Walleye. So he must be either Bear or Fly. So, let's begin to fill in the chart.

|      | Rabbit | Fly | Walleye | Bear |
|------|--------|-----|---------|------|
| Bob  |        |     |         |      |
| Bill |        |     |         |      |
| Pat  | O      | O   |         |      |
| Tom  | O      |     | O       |      |

From c, we know that Bob can't be Bear or Rabbit. Since he is faster than both Pat and Bear, Pat must be Walleye (since Pat was either Walleye or Bear).

As you can see from the final chart, Bill must be Rabbit, Tom has to be Bear, and Bob must be Fly.

|      | Rabbit | Fly | Walleye | Bear |
|------|--------|-----|---------|------|
| Bob  | O      | X   | O       | O    |
| Bill | X      | O   | O       | O    |
| Pat  | O      | O   | X       | O    |
| Tom  | O      | O   | O       | X    |

**373.** We know that Brand A and Brand B equal 40 pounds. We also know that 40 pounds times $7 a pound will equal $280. We can set up two equations that can be solved simultaneously.

$$A + B = 40 \text{ pounds}$$
$$9A + 4B = \$280$$

Multiply the first equation by −9 to cancel out the A's.

$$-9A - 9B = -360$$
$$\underline{9A + 4B = \phantom{-}280}$$
$$-5B = -80$$

B = 16 and, therefore, A = 24 pounds.

**374.** Here's how you figure it out.

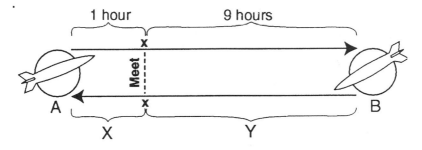

X + Y   = total distance
$V_f$  = velocity of faster rocket
$V_s$  = velocity of slower rocket
$T_b$  = time before meeting
Y   = velocity of the faster rocket multiplied by the time before they meet ($V_f \times T_b$)
X   = velocity of the slower rocket multiplied by the time before they meet ($V_s \times T_b$)

Therefore, $\dfrac{X}{Y} = \dfrac{V_s}{V_f}$

Now after the rockets meet, Y is equal to the slower velocity multiplied by 9, and X is equal to the faster velocity multiplied by one.

Thus: $\dfrac{X}{Y} = \dfrac{V_f}{9V_s}$

We now have two different fractions that represent $\frac{X}{Y}$, and they are equal.

$$\frac{V_s}{V_f} = \frac{V_f}{9V_s}$$
$$V^2_f = 9V^2_s$$
$$\sqrt{V^2_f} = \sqrt{9V^2_s}$$
$$V_f = 3V_s$$

The faster rocket is going three times as fast as the slower rocket.

**375.** Let's call the first system X and the second system Y.

| X | Y |
|---|---|
| 14 | 36 |
| 133 | 87 |

In order to get an idea of some relationship between the two systems, we'll subtract 14 from 133 (119) and compare that to the difference of 87 minus 36 (51). We can compare 119 to 51, but first, let's reduce it by dividing by 17, giving us 7 to 3. For every seven degrees on the X thermometer, Y will grow or decrease by three. When X is at 14°, if we move toward X becoming 0°, Y will be reduced by 6°. When X is 0°, Y = 30°, giving us the formula Y = $^3/_7$X + 30.

To find the temperature at which both thermometers read the same, set Y to equal X, and the formula then becomes:

$$X = {}^3/_7X + 30$$
$${}^4/_7X = 30$$
$$4X = 210$$
$$X = 52.5°$$

**376.** There are three different shapes to consider: a square, a loop, and two connecting lines. Figures A, B, and C each use two of the shapes. These first three figures form a pattern. Beginning with Figure D, the sequence continues. To get Figure D, Figure A was rotated 90° to the right. Figure E is really Figure B rotated 90° to the right. Therefore, the sixth figure will be Figure C rotated 90° to the right.

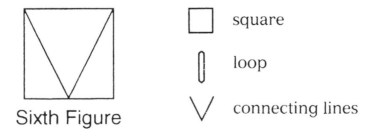

Sixth Figure

☐ square

loop

∨ connecting lines

**377.** The answer is D. The other four figures have both concave and convex components. Figure D has convex parts only.

**378.** The only thing you have to go on are the names of the people and the letters in their names. After a little inspection, you'll find each letter of the name is equivalent to three of "them," whatever "them" may be. Mary Les has seven letters in her name, therefore she has twenty-one of "them."

**379.** There are twenty-five individual cubes.

**380.** This is a good example of a problem or puzzle that can be broken into smaller components to determine a pattern.

If one person walks into a theater to take one seat, that person has only one choice. If two people occupy two seats, this can happen in two different ways. Three people occupying three seats (following the condition that each subsequent person sits next to another) can be accomplished in four different ways. Four people in four seats produce eight ways. We'll make a table to see what we have.

| Number of People | Possible Combinations |
|:---:|:---:|
| 1 | 1 |
| 2 | 2 |
| 3 | 4 |
| 4 | 8 |
| 5 | ? |

As can be seen, with each additional person and seat, the different orders increase by a power of two. For five people in five seats, there are sixteen different possible combinations. For any number N, it can be seen that $2^{(N-1)}$ will give the correct answer. So, for twelve people, 4096 different combinations are possible:

$$2^{(13-1)} = 2^{12} = 4096$$

**381.** There were 20 nickels and 20 dimes. To solve this, set up the following equations, where n = nickels and d = dimes:

$$n = d$$
$$.05n + .10d = 3.00$$
$$.05n + .10n = 3.00$$
$$.15n = 3.00$$
$$n = 20$$

**382.** $x = 5$, $y = 6$, and $z = 4$, so the sum is 15. The variable $x$ can be either 0 or 5. It must be 5 because there is no number that ends in 0 when multiplied by 7 ($y \times 7$, resulting in $x$). Therefore, a 3 is carried over to the $y$. Since $x$ is 5, $y$ must be 6 because $7 \times 6 = 42$. Add the 3 that was carried over and you get 45. Therefore, $z$ is 4.

**383.** It might be helpful to set up a grid as follows:

|        | Basketball | Football | Baseball |
|--------|------------|----------|----------|
| Alex   | x          |          | o        |
| Ryan   | o          |          |          |
| Steven | x          | o        | x        |

We can see that Ryan must like basketball since neither Alex nor Steven does. Steven does not like basketball or baseball, so he must like football, leaving Alex liking baseball.

**384.** Seven zips have the weight of 1 wob. The problem can be set up as follows:

$$26z = 4c + 2w$$
$$8z + 2c = 2w$$

Rearranging, we get

(1) $26z = 4c + 2w$

(2) $8z = -2c + 2w$

Multiply equation (2) by 2 so that the $c$ factor drops out, and combine the two equations:

$$
\begin{array}{rcl}
26z &=& 4c + 2w \\
\underline{16z} &=& \underline{-4c + 4w} \\
42z &=& 6w \\
7z &=& w
\end{array}
$$

**385.** Look before you leap

**386.** The missing number is 10. The numbers in each circle add up to 50.

**387.** The answer is 96. Set up the following equations:

$$\tfrac{1}{2} \times \tfrac{2}{3} \times \tfrac{3}{5} = \tfrac{6}{30} = \tfrac{1}{5}$$
$$\tfrac{1}{5} \times 240 = 48$$
$$48 \div \tfrac{1}{2} = 96$$

**388.** It's the right thing to do.

**389.** The answer is "three words."

**390.** The next letter is P. The letters missing between letters in the series form the pattern 1, 2, 1, 2, 1, 2…

**391.** Figure 4 is the only one that doesn't contain a triangle.

**392.** The lesser of two evils

**393.** It is impossible to average 60 miles per hour for this trip. At 30 miles per hour, the car would travel one mile in two minutes; at 60 miles per hour, the car would travel two miles in two minutes. So, in order to average 60 mph, the entire trip of two miles would have to be completed in two minutes. But the driver has already used two minutes going from point A to point B; there's not time left to get from point B to point C.

**394.** Here's one way to solve the puzzle:

TOOK
BOOK
BOON
BORN
BURN

**395.** 6.25 percent. Remember, length × width = area. Let $l$ = length and $w$ = width. Then

$$l + .25l = 1.25l$$
$$w - .25w = .75w$$
$$1.25l \times .75w = 93.75\underline{lw}$$

Finally,

$$100 - 93.75 = 6.25$$

**396.** The chances are 1 in 3. Here are all the possible draws (C1 = first cherry gumdrop, C2 = second cherry gumdrop, O = orange gumdrop):

| First draw | Second draw |
|---|---|
| C1 | C2 |
| C1 | O |
| C2 | C1 |
| C2 | O |
| O | C1 |
| O | C2 |

Among the six possible draws, O appears twice in the second draw column; thus the chances are 2 in 6, or 1 in 3.

**397.** Five.

**398.** The "R" goes above the line. The letters above the line are closed with a space inside them.

**399.** Time slips into the future

**400.** There are 100 years in a century.

**401.** Let $x$ = the fraction. Then:

$$(3 \times \tfrac{1}{4}x) \times x = \tfrac{1}{12}$$
$$3/4x2 = \tfrac{1}{12}$$
$$x2 = \tfrac{1}{9}$$
$$x = \tfrac{1}{3}$$

**402.** Two miles. They are actually eating up the distance at 120 miles per hour (50 + 70):

$$\frac{120 \text{ miles}}{60 \text{ minutes}} = \text{two miles in one minute}$$

**403.** Pocket full of money

**404.** They can be combined in 12 different ways.

**405.** $\tfrac{1}{24}$

$$\frac{3}{32} - \frac{1}{16} = \frac{1}{32}$$

$$4 \times \left( \frac{1}{3} \times \frac{1}{32} \right) = \frac{4}{96} \text{ or } \frac{1}{24}$$

**406.** The letters "mot" will create the words "mother," "motion," "motor," "motif," and "motto."

**407.** The answer is (e). Remember, $x$ may be a negative number.

**408.** He would have 20 pleezorns. Count the letters in each name and multiply by 2.

**409.** $.1 \times .9 \times .8 = .072 = 7.2\%$

**410.** Line dance

**411.** The ratio is 1 to 2. One way to solve this problem is to set up an equation in which $x$ equals the amount of $48 chemical used and $y$ equals the amount of $36 chemical used:

$$48x + 36y = 40(x + y)$$
$$48x + 36y = 40x + 40y$$
$$8x = 4y$$
$$\frac{x}{y} = \frac{1}{2}$$

**412.** Traffic jam

**413.** There are 31 triangles.

**414.** The ratio is 1 to 2. It might help to set up the problem as follows:

$$\frac{5x}{4y} = \frac{7}{8}$$
$$40x = 28y$$
$$10x = 7y$$

Thus, $10x$ to $7y$ is a 1-to-1 relationship. We are asked for the ratio of $10x$ to $14y$; since $14 = 7 \times 2$, we can see that it is a 1-to-2 relationship.

**415.** Don't count your chickens before they hatch.

**416.** Three-ring circus

**417.** Here are 21 four-letter words:

| | | |
|---|---|---|
| twin | wine | lint |
| kiln | kilt | lent |
| wink | wilt | like |
| link | welt | kine |
| tine | tile | lien |
| newt | kite | line |
| went | wile | knit |

**418.** The answer is 13,222.

$$12,000$$
$$+1,222$$
$$13,222$$

**419.** JJ. The letters are the initial letters of pairs of month names, starting with October-November.

**420.** Forward thinking

**421.** Double-decker sandwich

**422.** Draw a line as follows and you'll see the answer, June:

**423.** $4^6 + 6^4$ . . . by more than double

**424.** Microorganism

**425.** There is one wheel on a unicycle.

**426.** Fifteen angles of less than 90 degrees can be formed.

**427.** Here they are:

$$\frac{1}{2} = \frac{6,729}{13,458}$$

$$\frac{1}{3} = \frac{5,832}{17,496}$$

$$\frac{1}{4} = \frac{4,392}{17,568}$$

$$\frac{1}{5} = \frac{2,769}{13,845}$$

$$\frac{1}{6} = \frac{2,943}{17,658}$$

$$\frac{1}{7} = \frac{2,394}{16,758}$$

$$\frac{1}{8} = \frac{3,187}{25,496}$$

$$\frac{1}{9} = \frac{6,381}{57,429}$$

**428.** i before e except after c

**429.** The missing numbers are 18 and 5, respectively. There are actually two separate series of numbers in this puzzle. Look at every other number, beginning first with 8 and then with 15.

**430.** The value of z must be 9 in all cases.

**431.** The value of x is 1. The variable y can have any of a number of values, but x must always equal 1 and z must always equal 9.

**432.** Yes. A number is divisible by 8 if its last three digits are divisible by 8. Examples: 6,240; 9,184; 15,536.

**433.** Doorbell. All the rest have handles.

**434.** You would write it 17 times. Don't forget that there are two 4s in 44!

**435.** Figure C is the only figure without a straight line.

**436.** Right cross followed by an uppercut

**437.** For these three numbers, 455 is the lowest common denominator.

**438.** Fill in the blanks

**439.** 107 percent of 300 is greater. Because 107 percent is equivalent to 1.07, we have

$$1.07 \times 300 = 321$$
$$.50 \times 600 = 300$$

**440.** The answer is $^{10}/_{33}$. The problem can be solved as follows:

$$\cfrac{1}{3+\cfrac{1}{3\frac{1}{3}}} = \cfrac{1}{3+\cfrac{1}{\frac{10}{3}}} = \cfrac{1}{3+\frac{3}{10}} = \cfrac{1}{\frac{33}{10}} = \frac{10}{33}$$

**441.**

| 1 | 8 | 13 | 12 |
|---|---|----|----|
| 14 | 11 | 2 | 7 |
| 4 | 5 | 16 | 9 |
| 15 | 10 | 3 | 6 |

**442.** Here's one way:

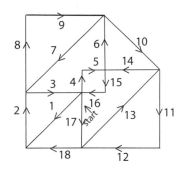

**443.** You would receive 221 silver pieces. If you were to exchange your kooklas only for gold, it would require 40 × 7 or 280 pieces. But there are only 161 gold pieces, leaving you 119 gold pieces short. The value of silver coins to gold coins is in the ratio of 13 to 7:

$$\frac{13}{7} = \frac{x}{119}$$

$$7x = 1,547$$

$$x = 1221$$

**444.** The missing number is 35. The second number in each box is the square of the first number minus 1.

**445.** There are 720 possible arrangements. Use the following equation to solve the problem (this is called factorial notation):

$$6! = 6 \times 5 \times 4 \times 3 \times 2 \times 1 = 720$$

**446.** Hole in one

**447.** The number 9 goes below the line and the number 10 goes above it—the numbers 1, 2, 6, and 10 are all spelled with three letters; the rest have four or more.

**448.** Your eyes are bigger than your stomach

**449.** Here are two examples:
1. When giving yes and no answers, a person who tells a lie about a lie is telling the truth.
2. Imagine a child rolling his wagon backward down a hill. If you were to film this and run the film backward, you would see the wagon going forward up the hill.

**450.** Algebra

**451.** $8\frac{88}{88}$

**452** There are 24 cubes.

**453.** They say at least 100 words can be made from "Thanksgiving." How many can you find?

**454.** It is $7/9$. The problem can be approached as follows:

$$1/10 \div 1/2 \div 1/5 = 1/10 \times 2 \times 5 = 1$$

$$1 \times 7/9 = 7/9$$

**455.** Elbow grease

**456.** $x$, $y$, and $z$ = 8, 12, and 60 pounds, respectively. Starting with the 8 ft. section:

$$8 \text{ ft.} \times 10 \text{ lbs.} = 80 \text{ ft.-lbs.}$$

To balance, the bottom left part of the mobile must also equal 80 ft.-lbs., so its total weight must be 20 lbs. (4 ft. × 20 lbs. = 80 ft.-lbs.) Therefore,

$$x + y = 20$$
$$\text{and}$$
$$6x = 4y.$$
$$\text{So, } y = 20 - x$$
$$\text{and substituting,}$$
$$6x = 4(20 - x)$$
$$6x = 80 - 4x$$
$$10x = 80$$
$$x = 8$$
$$\text{and therefore,}$$
$$y = 12.$$

Adding the total weights of the left side, we have

$$120 + 10 + 8 + 12 = 150 \text{ lbs.}$$
$$150 \text{ lbs.} \times 4 \text{ ft.} = 600 \text{ ft.-lbs.}$$

Therefore, the right side must also be 600 ft.-lbs.:

$$10 \text{ ft.} \times z \text{ lbs.} = 600 \text{ ft.-lbs.}$$
$$z = 60$$

**457.** All answers are divisible by nine.

**458.** The square is 6 feet by 6 feet. To solve this problem, let $x$ represent each side of the square. Then

$$4x = x^2 \times \frac{2}{3}$$
$$12x = 2x^2$$
$$6x = x^2$$
$$x = 6$$

**459.** Shrinking violets

**460.** 2 in 9. Because each die has 6 faces, there are 6 × 6 or 36 possible combinations of numbers. Of these, 6 combinations result in a 7:

6 and 1

1 and 6

5 and 2

2 and 5

4 and 3

3 and 4

And 2 combinations result in an 11:

5 and 6

6 and 5

thus the chances are 8 in 36, or 2 in 9.

**461.** Calm before the storm

**462.**

MOOD

MOON

MORN

BORN

BARN

**463.** T = 15. Since A = 2, we can substitute A into the first four equations to come up with the following:

$$(1) \quad 2 + B \qquad = H$$
$$(2) \quad H + P \qquad = T$$
$$(3) \quad T + 2 \qquad = F$$
$$(4) \quad B + P + F \quad = 30$$

Now substitute equation (1) into equation (2):

$$(2 + B) + P = T$$

Rearranging, we get

$$B + P = T - 2$$

Substitute this into equation (4):

$$(T - 2) + F = 30$$

Finally, substitute equation (3) into equation (4) and solve for T:

$$(T - 2) + (T + 2) = 30$$
$$2T = 30$$
$$T = 15$$

**464.** An onion costs 7 cents. Set up the equations, with $x$ as potatoes and $y$ as onions:

$$5x + 6y = 1.22$$
$$6x + 5y = 1.31$$

Multiply the first equation by 6, the second one by 5:
$$30x + 36y = 7.32$$
$$30x + 25y = 6.55$$
Subtract the second equation from the first, and you have:
$$0x + 11y = .77$$
$$y = .07$$

**465.** Rising tide

**466.** It can be done as follows:

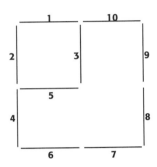

**467.** A: $\dfrac{343}{1000}$  B: $\dfrac{7}{24}$

On any given single draw with all 10 balls in the box, there is a 7 in 10 chance of drawing a green ball. So the probability of all 3 balls chosen being green is:

$$\frac{7}{10} \times \frac{7}{10} \times \frac{7}{10} = \frac{343}{1000} = 34.3\%$$

If the balls are not replaced in the bag:

The chance on the first draw is 7 in 10; on the second draw, it is 6 in 9; and on the third draw, it is 5 in 8. So the probability of 3 balls being in pulled in succession if they are not replaced is:

$$\frac{7}{10} \times \frac{6}{9} \times \frac{5}{8} = \frac{210}{720} \text{ or } \frac{7}{24} = 29.2\%$$

**468.** The missing number is zero. If you convert each fraction to twelfths, you get the following series:

$$\frac{5}{12} \quad \frac{4}{12} \quad \frac{3}{12} \quad \frac{2}{12} \quad \frac{1}{12} \quad 0$$

**469.** Multiplication tables

**470.** There are 206 bones in the human body.

**471.** Factors of the number 12 (6 + 4 + 3 + 2 + 1) add up to 16.

**472.** 18. ¼ of ⅓ of ⅙ is ¹⁄₇₂; ¹⁄₇₂ of 432 is 6; and 6 divided by ⅓ is 18.

**473.** Deep in thought

**474.** Fifty-six applicants have experience in selling both golf equipment and athletic shoes. Since 13 of the applicants have had no sales experience, we're dealing with 87 people who have some experience. Of the 87 applicants, 65 of them have sold golf equipment, which means that 22 of this group haven't sold golf equipment (87 − 65 = 22). Seventy-eight of the applicants have sold shoes, which means that 9 haven't (87 − 78 = 9). Therefore, we have 9 + 22 or 31 people who could not have sold both—thus, 87 − 31 = 56 people who *have* had experience in selling both.

**475.** 110 square yards. An area 11 yards square measures 11 yards on each of four sides and therefore has a total of 121 square yards. An area of 11 square yards, if it were square, would be just under 3.32 yards on each side. The difference between the two, then, is found by subtracting 11 square yards from 121 square yards: 110 square yards.

**476.** Life

**477.** You are on time

**478.** 6009, 6119

**479.** Seven. These are the elements hydrogen, carbon, and nitrogen, with their respective atomic numbers; seven is the atomic number for nitrogen.

**480.** Can't see the forest for the trees

**481.** They are 496 and 8,128. The next perfect number after that is 33,550,336!

**482.** There are 16 possibilities, each having a probability of ¹⁄₁₆. There are 6 ways with exactly 2 tails, 4 ways with 3 tails, and 1 way with 4 tails. That's a total of 11 ways out of 16. The chances are 11 in 16.

| | |
|---|---|
| HHHH | TTTT |
| HTTT | THHH |
| HHHT | TTTH |
| HTHH | THTT |
| HHTH | TTHT |
| HHTT | TTHH |
| HTHT | THTH |
| HTTH | THHT |

**483.** A break in the action

**484.** Let a smile be your umbrella.

**485.** 27,000. The repeating pattern is, respectively, 2, 3, and 5 times the preceding number.

**486.**

**487.** It will take 1.2 hours.

The equation can be set up this way:

$$\frac{x}{3} + \frac{x}{2} = 1$$

Multiply by 6:

$$2x + 3x = 6$$
$$5x = 6$$
$$x = \frac{6}{5} = 1.2$$

**488.** I am 19 years old and my sister is 9.

Let $x$ = my sister's age and $y$ = my age.

$$y = x + 10 \text{ and}$$
$$y + 1 = 2(x + 1)$$
$$y = 2x + 1$$

Substituting this result in our first equation, we have

$$2x + 1 = x + 10$$
$$x = 9$$
$$\text{so}$$
$$y = 19.$$

When my sister was 5, I was 3 times older than she was.

**489.** The missing letter is S. These are the first letters of the even numbers when spelled out, beginning with two.

**490.** Upside-down cake

**491.** Sally Billingsley and Susie Jenkins are the real names. Because one of the first two statements had to be false, the third statement also had to be false.

**492.** The square of 95 is 9,025. There are several ways this can be done. Here's one way. It helps to remember that any number ending in 5, when squared, will always end in 25.

Go to the number ending in 0 directly above the number ending in 5—in this case 100. Now go to the number ending in 0 directly below the number ending in 5—in this case 90.

In your mind square 100 (10,000) and square 90 (8,100). Add these two numbers together (18,100) and divide by 2 (9,050); then replace the last two digits with 25. So the square of 95 is 9,025.

Now, come up with another way to do this.

**493.** The missing letter is N; the word is "sandwich."

**494.** Power surge

**495.** None. Instead, turn the puzzle upside-down and add:

$$
\begin{array}{r}
86 \\
91 \\
+68 \\
\hline
245
\end{array}
$$

**496.** 20 percent. Say there are 10 caramels. Since the number of caramels is 25 percent of the number of other candies, there must be 40 pieces of candy that aren't caramels. The total number of pieces of candy = 10 + 40 = 50, so $^{10}/_{50} = ^{1}/_{5}$ = 20 percent.

**497.** Fender bender

**498.** There are 118 elements in the periodic table.

**499.** Here's one way to solve the puzzle:

ROAD
ROAM
ROOM
LOOM
LOOP

**500.** Diagram E is the odd one out. The other four are symmetrical about both of their axes; if you turn them 90 degrees, they will look the same as in their original positions.

**501.**

| C | = | 100 |
|---|---|---|
| D | = | 500 |
| M | = | 1,000 |
| $\overline{V}$ | = | 5,000 |
| $\overline{X}$ | = | 10,000 |
| $\overline{L}$ | = | 50,000 |
| $\overline{C}$ | = | 100,000 |
| $\overline{D}$ | = | 500,000 |
| $\overline{M}$ | = | 1,000,000 |

**502.** Current affair

**503.** Here are some 10-letter words.

| | | |
|---|---|---|
| Typewriter | Proprietor | Tetterwort |
| Pepperroot | Pirouetter | Repertoire |
| Pepperwort | Prerequire | Perpetuity |

**504.** Central Intelligence Agency

**505.** The chances are still 1 in 50.

**506.** The missing number is $^1/_{30}$. The series is constructed as follows:

$$12 = ^1/_7 \text{ of } 84$$
$$2 = ^1/_6 \text{ of } 12$$
$$^2/_5 = ^1/_5 \text{ of } 2$$
$$^1/_{10} = ^1/_4 \text{ of } ^2/_5$$
$$^1/_{30} = ^1/_3 \text{ of } ^1/_{10}$$

**507.** Guilty beyond a reasonable doubt

**508.** $96. Use the equation

$$^1/_4x - (^3/_4 \times ^1/_4x) = \$6$$
$$^1/_4x - ^3/_{16}x = \$6$$

Multiply each side by 16:

$$4x - 3x = \$96$$
$$x = \$96$$

**509.** She is their aunt.

**510.** "Lapy" means tree. From the first two phrases, "rota" must mean apple. From the third phrase, "mena" must mean large, leaving "lapy" to be tree.

**511.** Hologram

**512.** The numbers in each circle add up to 150, so the missing number is 23.

**513.** The missing number is 7. The numbers have a one-to-one correspondence with the letters of the alphabet, where A = 1, B = 2, C = 3, and so forth. The word spelled out is "mind-bending."

**514.** No time left on the clock

**515.** Book

**516.** There are 180 degrees in a triangle.

**517.** The chance of drawing the ace of spades is 1 in 52; for the king, 1 in 51; for the queen, 1 in 50; and for the jack, 1 in 49. To calculate the answer, multiply these altogether:

$^1/_{52} \times ^1/_{51} \times ^1/_{50} \times ^1/_{49} = ^1/_{6,497,400}$

**518.**

$^{34}/_{650}$ or $^{17}/_{325}$

$^1/_{10}$ less than $^3/_{13}$ is:

$^{30}/_{130} - ^{13}/_{130} = ^{17}/_{130}$

4 times $^1/_{10}$ of that number is:

$4 \times ^1/_{10} \times ^{17}/_{130} = ^4/_{10} \times ^{17}/_{130}$

$\quad\quad = ^2/_{50} \times ^{17}/_{130}$

$\quad\quad = ^{34}/_{650}$

$\quad\quad = ^{17}/_{325}$

**519.**

$$\begin{array}{r} 70,839 \\ - 6,458 \\ \hline 64,381 \end{array}$$

The answer to the "SEND + MORE = MONEY" puzzle is:

$$\begin{array}{r} 9,567 \\ + 1,085 \\ \hline 10,652 \end{array}$$

**520.** There are 19 squares.

**521.** Slim chance

**522.** Knock on wood

**523.**

BIKE
BITE
MITE
MATE
MATH

**524.** POTS, SPOT, and OPTS. These are the only three remaining four-letter words that can be made by using the letters O, P, S, and T only once.

**525.** The missing number is 6. Keep taking the differences between numbers (keeping in mind positive and negative differences) and you get:

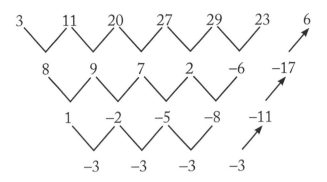

**526.** Transparent

**527.** Dirty Dozen

**528.** With players for each match through six rounds, $2^6$ or $6^4$ players are entered.

**529.** There are 24 letters in the Greek alphabet.

**530.** Five. Square 1 is the largest square and frames the whole figure. Then square 2 is placed in the lower right corner, and square 3 is placed in the upper left corner. (Square 2 and square 3 are the same size.) Square 4 is placed over square 3 in the upper-left corner, and square 5 is placed in the middle.

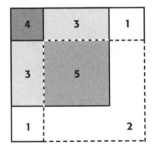

**531.** Each layer would contain a number of balls equal to the square of the layer. In other words, layer 1 (the top layer) would have $1^2$ = 1 ball; layer 2 would have $2^2$ = 4 balls; layer 3 would have $3^2$ = 9 balls; and so on. The layers would stack up like this, for a total of 140 balls.

$$
\begin{array}{r}
1 \\
4 \\
9 \\
16 \\
25 \\
36 \\
+\ 49 \\
\hline
140
\end{array}
$$

**532.** Close shave

**533.** Starting with the bottom row, determine if two adjacent circles are different colors. A black circle goes above and between different-colored circles. A white circle goes above and between same-colored circles. The top of the pyramid is shown below.

**534.** From left to right, the weights are 200 lbs., 120 lbs., 102 lbs., and 68 lbs.

First we find the two weights on the left. Their total weight (call it $a$) at a distance of 4 ft. must balance 160 lbs. at a distance of 8 ft.:

$$4a = 8 \times 160$$
$$a = 1{,}280 \div 4 = 320 \text{ lbs.}$$

Then $5/8$ of this weight at 3 ft. must balance $3/8$ of this weight at 5 ft.:

$$\frac{5}{8} \times 320 = 200 \text{ lbs. and } \frac{3}{8} \times 320 = 120 \text{ lbs.}$$

Next we find the two weights on the right. Their total weight (call it b) at a distance of 12 ft. must balance 200 + 120 + 160 + 30 = 510 lbs. at a distance of 4 ft.:

$$12b = 4 \times 510$$
$$b = 2040 \div 12 = 170 \text{ lbs.}$$

Then $6/10$ of this weight at 4 ft. must balance $4/10$ of this weight at 6 ft.:

$$\frac{6}{10} \times 170 = 102 \text{ lbs. and } \frac{4}{10} \times 170 = 68 \text{ lbs.}$$

**535.** The proof is in the pudding

**536.** Four people can sit in five seats as follows:

$$5 \times 4 \times 3 \times 2, \text{ for a total of 120 different ways.}$$

**537.** Shine

**538.** The best approach to this problem is to find a common denominator of 2, 4, and 7 that is less than 30—that is, 28. Then add up the calculated numbers of students:

> 2 students received a B
> ¼ of 28 = 7 students failed
> ½ of 28 = 14 students received a D
> $\frac{1}{7}$ of 28 = 4 students received a C

totalling 27, which means only 1 student received an A.

**539.** 1 day. Let $x$ be the number of days it would take all three to build the fence. In 1 day the total of their individual contributions to building the fence would be:

$$\frac{x}{2} + \frac{x}{3} + \frac{x}{6} = 1$$
$$\frac{3x}{6} + \frac{2x}{6} + \frac{x}{6} = \frac{6}{6}$$
$$6x = 6$$
$$x = 1 \text{ day}$$

**540.** Foreign correspondent

**541.** 441. Use the following formula to find the number of cubes when the width, length, and height of the stack have the same number of cubes.

Let c = that number of cubes.

$$c^3 + (c - 1)^3 + (c - 2)^3 + (c - 3)^3 \ldots (c - c)^3$$
$$\text{So,}$$
$$6^3 + 5^3 + 4^3 + 3^3 + 2^3 + 1^3 =$$
$$216 + 125 + 64 + 27 + 8 + 1 = 441$$
$$\text{total cubes.}$$

**542.** Here's one way. Can you find others?

|   |    |   |
|---|----|---|
| 2 | 10 |   |
| 5 | 8  | 6 |
| 3 | 1  | 4 |
|   | 9  | 7 |

**543.** 4 to 1. Here is one way to solve this:

$$\text{if } p = \tfrac{3}{4}q, \text{ then } q = \tfrac{4}{3}p$$

$$\text{if } q = \tfrac{2}{3}r, \text{ then } r = \tfrac{3}{2}q \text{ and}$$

$$\text{if } r = \tfrac{1}{2}s, \text{ then } s = \tfrac{2}{1}r$$

Therefore,

$$s \text{ to } p \text{ is } \frac{2}{1} \times \frac{3}{2} \times \frac{4}{3} = \frac{24}{6} = 4 \text{ to } 1$$

**544.** Safety in numbers

**545.**  first base: Reggie
catcher: Lou
right field: Leo
left field: Chris

Here's how to deduce the answer from the given facts:

Reggie: From the question, we know that Reggie can't play right field. From point (a) we know that Reggie isn't the catcher or the left fielder, so he must be the first baseman.

Leo: From the question, we know that Leo can't be the catcher, and from point (b) we know that Leo can't be the left fielder. He can't play first base because that's Reggie's position, so he must be the right fielder.

Lou: From the question, we know that Lou can't play left field. He can't play first base (Reggie's position) or right field (Leo's position), so he must be the catcher.

Chris: With all the other positions filled, Chris must be the left fielder.

**546.** Golden anniversary

**547.** The letter e.

**548.**

BAND
BIND
BINS
PINS
PIPS

**549.** 2 to 3. Let the bicycle's current age be $3x$ making the tires' age $x$ when the bicycle was old as the tires are now. To make them the same age we must add to the tires' age some number, $y$, and subtract from the bicycle's age the same number, $y$:

$$\underline{\text{bike's age}} \quad \underline{\text{tires' age}}$$
$$2x - y = x + y$$
$$2x = 2y$$
$$x = y$$

Since we've already established that x = y, we can substitute y for x in the bike's current age:

$$3x = 3y$$

The tires' current age is then 2y, and the ratio of the tires' current age to the bicycle's current age is 2y/3y, a ratio of 2 to 3.

**550.** $2^{13}$, by a lot.

$$2^{13} = 8,192$$
$$\text{but}$$
$$2^{12} + 2^2 = 4,096 + 4 = 4,100$$

**551.** Four score and seven years ago

**552.** Repeating rifles

**553.**

$$
\begin{array}{r}
73544 \\
73544 \\
73544 \\
+494046 \\
\hline
714678
\end{array}
$$

**554.** Number the grids as shown below, designating the row and column of each box. The sum of the numbers in the marked boxes in the first grids (11 + 21 and 12 + 31) equal the numbers in the marked boxes in the second grids (32 and 43, respectively).

|    | 12 | 13 |
|----|----|----|
|    | 22 | 23 |
| 31 |    | 33 |

| 11 |    | 13 | 14 |
|----|----|----|----|
| 21 | 22 | 23 | 24 |
|    | 32 | 33 | 34 |
| 41 | 42 |    | 44 |

**555.** Connect the dots

**556.** $9 \times 8 \times 7 \times 6 \times 5 \times 4 \times 3 \times 2 \times 1 = 362{,}880$ different seating arrangements. In mathematics, this is written "9!" and called "factorial 9."

**557.**

| | |
|---|---|
| 1. gambol | k. frolic |
| 2. fortissimo | c. loud |
| 3. sortie | l. raid |
| 4. millinery | b. hats |
| 5. culinary | i. cooking |
| 6. ornithology | n. birds |
| 7. odoriferous | f. smell |
| 8. gustatory | o. taste |
| 9. humus | m. soil |
| 10. terrapin | a. turtle |
| 11. bovine | j. cow |
| 12. antipodes | h. opposites |
| 13. equivocal | e. ambiguous |
| 14. potentate | d. power |
| 15. urbane | g. refined |

**558.** There is sufficient information. The ladder is 25 feet long. A diagram helps in the solution:

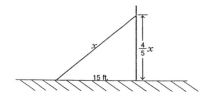

The ladder leaning against the wall makes a triangle. Let's call the ladder's length $x$. Since the top slid down to a point four-fifths of the ladder's length up the wall, we know that that side is $^4/_5 X$. The base of the triangle is 15 feet, which is the distance the foot of the ladder slid along the ground. Using the Pythagorean theorem ($c^2 = a^2 + b^2$), we can find the length of the ladder:

$$x^2 = (^4/_5 \, x)^2 + 225$$

$$x^2 = {}^{16}/_{25} \, x^2 + 225$$

$$25x^2 = 16x^2 + 5625$$

$$9x^2 = 5625$$

$$x^2 = 625$$

$$x = 25 \text{ ft.}$$

**559.** 70.

        1f = 10k
        1c = 6f = 6 × 10k = 60k
        1w = 5c = 5 × 60k = 300k
        1n = 7w = 7 × 300k = 2100k

Thus, there are 2100 krits in a nood. We also see that

        1w = 300k = 30(10k) = 30f

Therefore, there are 30 fligs in a wirp.

**560.** Two wrongs don't make a right.

**561.** Out to lunch

**562.** MMCDXLIV

**563.** 162 and 1.

Starting at left, every other number is multiplied by 3. Starting at right, every other number is also multiplied by 3.

**564.** $4^4 + 44 = 300$

**565.** It would appear in column B. Divide by 7 whatever number you wish to place, and see what the remainder is. If the remainder is 1, the number goes in column A; if the remainder is 2, the number goes in column B; and so on. (If the remainder is zero, however, the number goes in column G.)

**566.** Audrey will reach the destination first. Suppose they cover 12 miles, both walking at a rate of 2 miles per hour and running at a rate of 6 miles per hour. Use the formula $rt$ = d (rate × time = distance) to find each person's time.

Nancy (walks half the distance and runs half the distance):

$2t$ = 6 mi., so $t$ = 3 hrs. walking

$6t$ = 6 mi., so $t$ = 1 hr. running

$t$ = 4 hours total time

Audrey (walks half the time and runs half the time):

$$2(\tfrac{1}{2}t) + 6(\tfrac{1}{2}t) = 12 \text{ mi.}$$
$$t + 3t = 12$$
$$4t = 12$$
$$t = 3 \text{ hours total time}$$

**567.** Each reads the same when held upside down.

**568.** Lead by example

**569.** Simply add the sum of the two digits in any number to the sum of the two digits in the adjacent number to get the corresponding number in the row below. For example:

$$8 + 9 \ (89) \text{ and } 5 + 3 \ (53) = 25$$
$$5 + 3 \ (53) \text{ and } 1 + 7 \ (17) = 16$$

To find the missing number, add:

$$1 + 6 \ (16) \text{ and } 1 + 7 \ (17) = 15$$

**570.** His younger daughter received more—$4,000 more—than the older daughter. One way to solve this is to set up an equation that represents who received what:

$$x = \tfrac{1}{3} + \tfrac{1}{5}x + \tfrac{1}{6}x + \tfrac{1}{x} + 9{,}000$$

$$x = \frac{10}{30}x + \frac{6}{30}x + \frac{5}{30}x + 9{,}000$$

$$x = \frac{21}{30}x + 9{,}000$$

Multiplying both sides of the equation by $\frac{30}{9}$ , we get

$$\frac{30}{9}x = \frac{21}{9}x + \frac{270{,}000}{9}$$

$$\frac{30}{9}x - \frac{21}{9}x = 30{,}000$$

$$x = 30{,}000$$

Then

$$\frac{1}{3}x = \$10,000 \text{ (wife)}$$

$$\frac{1}{5}x = \$6,000 \text{ (son)}$$

$$\frac{1}{6}x = \$5,000 \text{ (older daughter)}$$

**571.** The missing number is 4. Simply add the first and second rows together to get the third row, like this:

$$
\begin{array}{r}
65,927 \\
\underline{14,354} \\
80,281
\end{array}
$$

**572.** In 60 days. If one clock gains a minute a day (or loses, the math will be the same), it will gain 24 minutes the first day, 48 minutes by the end of the second, and 120 minutes after 5 days. This means in ten days it will gain 4 hours and in 20 days, 8 hours. This times 3, to make it 24 hours, will require 60 days. The other clock running backward will tell the same time as the normal clock every 24 hours, so it really doesn't present a problem for the solution of the puzzle.

**573.** Cheaper by the dozen

**574.** Pages 6, 19, and 20 are also missing. Newspapers are printed double-sided, two pages to a sheet. The first and second pages are attached to the second-to-last and last pages—in this case, pages 23 and 24. The rest of the pages are attached as follows:

1–2 with 23–24
3–4 with 21–22
5–6 with 19–20
7–8 with 17–18
9–10 with 15–16
11–12 with 13–14

**575.** The value of *c* is 14. To solve the problem, set up the following equations:

$$(1) \; a + b = 13$$
$$(2) \; b + c = 22$$
$$(3) \; a + c = 19$$

Solve for b in equation (1):

$$b = 13 - a$$

Substitute this into equation (2):

$$13 - a + c = 22$$
$$-a + c \quad = 9$$

Then combine equations (2) and (3) and solve for *c*:

$$-a + c = 9$$
$$\underline{a + c = 19}$$
$$2c = 28$$
$$c = 14$$

**576.** Rotate the first square 90 degrees to the right to obtain the second square.

|   |   |   |
|---|---|---|
|   | X |   |
| X |   |   |
|   |   | X |

**577.**

MOVE
MORE
MARE
BARE
BARK

**578.** Sarah is the second-oldest; Liz is the oldest.

**579.** The missing number is 14. The first and last numbers added together make 19, as do the second number and the next-to-last number. Moving toward the middle in this fashion, each successive pair of numbers adds up to 19.

# ALSO AVAILABLE

*The Big Book of Brainteasers*

*Simple Sudoku*

*Lazy Weekend Crosswords*

*Brain Workout: Math & Logic Puzzles*

*Brain Workout: Word Search*